A History of
PENLEIGH

From Italian Prisoner-of-War Camp
to 21st Century Technology

by

Fred Davis MBE

Edited by

Kevin Eyres MA

THALES

Thales UK

2 Dashwood Lang Road, The Bourne Business Park,
Addlestone, Weybridge, Surrey. KT15 2NX
Tel: +44 (0)1932 824800 Fax: +44 (0)1932 824887

© Thales UK Limited 2011
November 2011

Project Manager	Angharad Jones
Design and Layout	Jane Kurle
Cover Design	John Entwistle
Proof-reader	Angela Thyer

Thales UK
Horizon House, Throop Road, Templecombe, Somerset. BA8 0DH
Tel: +44 (0)1963 370551 Fax: +44 (0)1963 372709

Researcher	David Crowcombe
Researcher and Proof-reader	Tim Wallis

Printed by St Andrew's Press, St. Andrews Park,
Princes Road, Wells, Somerset. BA5 1TE

Preface from Alex Dorrian CBE

Britain has a history of technological innovation, and the history of the Penleigh site in Wells is an example of how technology and industry have developed and changed during the last 75 years.

The Penleigh site has been involved in some very exciting technological innovations that have contributed to the defence of the UK and its civilian infrastructure. Thales is proud to have contributed to this technological evolution. We continue to employ, as did our predecessor companies, engineers, researchers and others who have the unique capability to design, develop and deploy equipment, systems and services that meet the most complex and exacting requirements.

This book has been written following our decision to relocate our business from the Penleigh site. This was a very difficult decision. However, we need to ensure that Thales remains competitive and responsive to our customers and stays competitive in very challenging markets. People are key to our success and it is crucial that we retain their considerable skill and experience. For this reason we have invested in modern, high-tech facilities at another Thales site in Somerset, to continue our proud history of innovation.

We are grateful to the people of Wells for their support over the years and this book provides a unique opportunity to capture an important part of their rich history.

Alex Dorrian CBE
Chairman Thales UK

This book is dedicated to the endeavour, hard work and achievements of the people who have worked at Penleigh.

We thank Vince Smith, MD, Air Operations, Thales UK for his foresight, his appreciation of people and their endeavours and achievements, and his awareness of the importance of history to a community, which enabled this book to be produced.

We wish to express gratitude to the following.

Fred Davis MBE for taking the time to write this book.

Dave Crowcombe for the hours, days, weeks and months of research and gathering of information.

Tim Wallis for his research and technical expertise.

Kevin Eyres MA for his editing expertise.

The Wells Journal for permission to use material from their archives and for their time and support.

We will always be indebted to the people of Wells, the Italian community, the numerous past and current members of staff who have so willingly shared their experiences, their momentoes, their photographs and some personal treasures that contribute so much to this book. So many people have been involved, and we thank each and every one.

Contents

Acknowledgements and Copyright

The author and publisher gratefully acknowledge the permission granted to reproduce the copyright material in this book. Every effort has been made to trace copyright holders and to obtain their permission for the use of copyright material. The publisher apologises for any errors or omissions and would be grateful for the notification of any corrections that should be incorporated in future reprints or editions of this book.

The author and publisher wish to thank the following for permission to reproduce copyright material.

Tom Genova for use of material from his web site featuring the history of Scophony-Baird; including images of early products. Nick Waloff, son of Demitri Waloff who was working for Scophony in London and Wells from 1939 onwards, for permission to reproduce extracts from his father's diaries. Nick's help and support in writing the early history of those companies was invaluable.

A special acknowledgement must go to the Mid Somerset Series of Newspapers for their help and support in researching their newspapers for the period covered by this book.

The book would have been the poorer had it not been for the help and support of David Crowcombe who acted as my 'leg man', interviewing past employees, collecting photographs and identifying the names of those featured. On the technical side Tim Wallis, who accompanied David, interpreted the many baffling subjects into plain English.

Fred Davis MBE

CHAPTER ONE

'I've been here so long that I'm almost a local ...'

As you drive out of the ancient cathedral city of Wells in Somerset it would be easy to miss the small group of one and two-storey buildings at the point where the city boundary gives way to the countryside. Whether by accident or design, these brick buildings with their russet-brown roofs blend into their setting in a way that modern industrial units could never do.

Since the late 1930s this twelve acre development has been known as the Penleigh site, and this book is its story.

UNDERWOOD QUARRY

The story begins in the nineteenth century when the site was no more than a small patchwork of fields in the rural manor of Penleigh. Local people describe childhood memories of a field sliced by the rusting remains of Victorian engineering. In fact, this was the remains of a conveyor belt system that carried stone and ballast from Underwood Quarry to the railway line that skirted Penleigh. These conveyor systems were a common sight at quarries in the Mendip Hills.

In the mid to late nineteenth century the railway network was rapidly expanding across the countryside of Britain, creating an insatiable demand for the ballast that the railway tracks lay on. The Mendip Hills were a rich source of ballast and road stone, and Underwood Quarry, together with a number of other local quarries were developed to take advantage of this.

The site was owned and operated by the local authority and road stone cut from Underwood Quarry was transported across the West Country, in bright red railway wagons, bearing the legend Somerset County Council, Underwood Quarries, Wells.

A Somerset County Council railway mineral wagon   © Burnham and District Model Railway Club

When the quarries were silent, having served their purpose, Somerset County Council was left owning tracts of land throughout the county for which it no longer had a specific use. The Penleigh site was just such a piece of land.

THE APPROACH OF WAR

In the 1930s the City of Wells must have seemed a long way from London and the industrial powerhouses of the Midlands and the North. A small city of no more than a few thousand souls, Wells had been quietly going about its business as a prosperous market town in the rolling Mendip Hills since it was granted the status of a city in 1205.

However, by 1939 the shadow of war that hung over the country could not be ignored, even in this quiet backwater. As the authorities in Britain prepared for war, plans were being made to house the inevitable influx of prisoners of war (POWs).

As part of this plan, the Mendip Hills were designated as a 'reception area'; and Somerset County Council handed over part of the Penleigh site to the Ministry of Works to accommodate a prisoner-of-war camp. This was to become No.107 (G) POW Camp, Penleigh, Wells.

RAF aerial photograph of Penleigh Camp and Underwood Quarry taken in 1946　　© English Heritage

Britain faced another threat as war approached. The German Luftwaffe could by now threaten virtually anywhere in the British Isles with a new kind of terror, the blitz. Plans were quickly drawn up to evacuate children from large conurbations to safety, and at the same time many small to medium sized businesses began to think seriously about relocating from the industrial heartlands to safer locations.

Because of its relative proximity to Bristol, Bath, and the capital, all potential targets for German bombers, Wells began to attract both evacuees and small businesses.

Norman Sanders was evacuated to Wells when he was nine years old. Amongst his recollections of that time he remembers having his first ever cup of coffee from Italian POWs working on the moors around North Wootton:

> *"We used to go down on the moors and the English sergeant was often asleep up against a tree. The Italians made us coffee and in return we stole soap from home for the Italians. We began to realise that even the enemies were human beings. The Italians never tried to escape."*

PRISONERS OF WAR

The Penleigh prisoner-of-war camp, which consisted of a large number of single-storey billet-style 'huts', was used mainly to hold Italian POWs.

Soldiers captured in African desert campaigns were the first to arrive. Once they had been settled at the camp, they could be seen working on farms in the area; some 'living in' and others being collected each day from the camp.

German prisoners of war working on a nearby farm

Prisoners of war from Penleigh Camp pictured at Stoke Lane Quarry, Stoke St Michael

Penleigh was not the only POW camp in the Wells area. In 1943 American troops constructed Stoberry Park Camp, just down the road from Penleigh. The camp's boundaries coincided with today's Stoberry Park housing estate, and an aerial photograph of the time shows some two dozen huts of varying sizes that accommodated 300 prisoners.

By 'D-day' the Americans had left, and fresh arrivals moved into Stoberry. Most were Italians who, like their counterparts at Penleigh, were soon put to work on the land and in the quarries.

After the Normandy landings, German prisoners began to arrive in large numbers, brought principally to work on the land, and because of a shortage of accommodation at Stoberry Park, a further satellite camp was set up at Maesbury.

In March 1944 there were only 2,550 German prisoners in the UK, but the figure climbed rapidly and peaked at 402,200 by September 1946. Stoberry Camp started holding German prisoners in 1945, and at that time it was described as a 'German Working Company' camp where POWs were employed in agriculture and forestry.

In October 1946 the Ministry of Health confirmed that the satellite camp at Maesbury was still fully occupied by German prisoners; and by late 1946 German prisoners had largely replaced the Italians at Penleigh who had repatriated in mid-1946.

WORKING PARTIES

The quarries in the Mendip Hills were particularly hard hit by the outbreak of war as experienced quarrymen were called up to fight for their country. POWs from Penleigh took over their jobs; familiar local names being replaced by unpronounceable ones such as Brenzeisler, Gahlert, Goldschmitt and Vanderveld. These inexperienced and often less than willing prisoners inevitably caused productivity to suffer.

One notable exception was Walter Czerny who remained in Somerset after the war continuing his employment at Moons Hill Quarry, Stoke St Michael. Walter went on to become the materials engineer for Somerset County Council.

Walter Czerny at work in Moons Hill Quarry

Six prisoners were employed at Moons Hill Quarry where Walter was based. They worked eight hours a day, Monday to Friday, and four hours on Saturday mornings – a total working week of forty-four hours. Each prisoner was paid one shilling and three farthings per hour (a little over five new pence per hour).

Every morning, local farmers drove the prisoners from Penleigh to their places of work and in the evening returned them to the camp, the cost of the journey to and from work being deducted from their wages bill.

ROMULUS AND REMUS

One particular prisoner at the Penleigh camp was Gaetano Celestra, who before the war had been a builder and mason. In 1941 Gaetano was fighting the British at Tobruk, where he was captured, ending up as a POW in Somerset, far from the blue skies and deep blue seas of his home.

Gaetano was employed at Beechbarrow Farm, Hillgrove, near Wells when a bomb fell in the field next to the farm buildings, destroying the wall running along the main Bristol to Wells road, and leaving a deep crater.

On summer evenings, in his spare time, and on Sundays, Gaetano set about rebuilding the wall, and immediately in front of the crater, he erected a statue of Romulus and Remus being suckled by a she-wolf, the symbol of Rome.

At the time Gaetano told the *Wells Journal* that the work had taken him three months, but he felt that he must do it. He said:

Romulus and Remus   © *Thales UK Ltd*

"I have learned to love England and the Mendips. I wanted to do something to show my gratitude for the kindness I have had from my employer and the people round here. I am very happy in England and I want to be English. I am hoping to get my naturalisation papers through soon."

The statue stands on a pedestal alongside the A39 at Pen Hill; an inscription on the base records its purpose to 'commemorate the kindness shown to POWs during their internment in the Wells area'.

After the war, Gaetano settled in the area and continued working as a builder and stonemason.

A FOCUS FOR THE ITALIAN COMMUNITY

In 2002 local builders D'ovidio Bros Ltd restored the monument, and by 2008 Mendip District Council had successfully applied for special protection for Gaetano's Romulus and Remus.

The conservation team's case stressed that the statue demonstrated the important legacy of the prisoner-of-war camps, and was of social and cultural importance in Mendip.

In his report, conservation officer Ian Gething stated:

"The statue continues to be an important focus for the Italian community in Wells and is a unique reminder of this period of the city's history.

It has been the focus of recent festivities, and there have been communications between Wells and Italian officials, including the country's president, in respect of the statue, its social, cultural and historical significance."

Councillor John Osman, who was responsible for regeneration and conservation, said:

"It is an important commemorative structure which celebrates the relationships and friendships that were forged between two opposing communities during the Second World War, and continues to be a symbol of the strengthening friendships at both local and international levels.

You only have to look around the local area to see the number of Italians who have settled in the Mendips, many of whom are relations of prisoners of war, and many of these current residents see this as a very important local feature."

Today, the statue of Romulus and Remus remains a tangible reminder of the early days of the Penleigh site. Securing its status as 'of special architectural or historic interest' means that it will be protected from deterioration or the threat of demolition.

ESCAPE

On August 30, 1946 the *Wells Journal* reported that two German POWs had escaped during the night from Penleigh Camp and were missed following the 7am roll-call. The paper noted that:

> *"One was a 25-year old German paratrooper, and the other a former member of the German navy, aged 23. Both were dressed in prisoner clothing with distinguishing marks."*

The following Friday the two prisoners gave themselves up at Minehead. They had called at the house of Mrs Roy James, wife of a Minehead taxi proprietor, who lived about a mile from the town.

Mrs James told the journal's reporter:

> *"In pouring rain the men, wearing macs, came to the front door and said they wanted to give themselves up. They were obviously all in and said they had not had a meal apart from what they had been able to scrounge since Monday.*
>
> *One of my visitors gave them a cigarette while we were waiting for the police to come. The Germans told us they were former members of the Air Force, though not fliers, and that they had been prisoners in America for three years. They tried to escape because, they said they were told when they left America that they were being taken home and instead they were landed in England. They also said they had better food in America than they are getting here."*

After being held overnight at Minehead Police Station the Germans were escorted back to the Penleigh Camp.

POST-WAR

With the end of the war, the treatment of POWs became more relaxed.

The *Wells Journal* of November 15, 1946 records that about 30 German prisoners attended the remembrance service at the Elim Gospel Church, standing with the rest of the congregation for the two minute silence. And on Christmas morning, more than 100 German prisoners attended the Christmas service. A German choir of 20 voices sang *Silent Night* and other carols; and 'a German prisoner officiated at the organ'.

By the start of 1947 POW teams were even allowed to play football matches against civilian clubs; and in July 1947 the city council proposed that German prisoners be allowed to use the swimming bath from 8pm to 9pm, one evening a week, but should not be allowed as spectators.

Mr Alderman Cocks 'thought the time had come for bygones to be bygones and the prisoners treated as humans'. Indeed, American troops, and Italian and German prisoners all expressed their gratitude for the kindness shown to them by the local residents.

In the autumn 1947, the *Wells Journal* outlined the remaining restrictions. Prisoners, for example, were still forbidden to enter licensed premises or to wear civilian outer garments. They were, however, permitted to use public transport within a five-mile radius of the camp.

All prisoners still had to be back in camp or their billets by 10pm. This was a practical precaution as much as anything, as in August 1947, a German POW had been cited as the co-respondent in a local divorce petition.

A year earlier in 1946, the abuse of these more relaxed conditions by Italian prisoners was reported to the Wells City Council. The complaints referred to 'unacceptable behaviour', which included obstruction of the pavements in the city.

The council immediately wrote to the Camp Commandant protesting against the 'general deportment of the Italians and the molesting of womenfolk and children'. The Commandant replied that he had issued instructions that the Italians should not assemble in groups of more than two, and had reminded them that they should show 'proper courtesy to all civilians'.

The letter continued:

"I have myself noticed certain Italians wearing civilian clothes of various kinds at times and I regret to say that this is the fault of the local farmers who have given the Italians these articles and allowed them to leave their farms wearing these items of clothing against the regulations.

No Italian is allowed to walk out from camp unless properly dressed in government provided uniform. I am reminding farmers who have prisoners billeted with them that they are responsible for seeing that Italians comply with the regulations."

As for the molestation of women and children, the Camp Commandant wrote rather drily:

"The regulations covering the behaviour of prisoners of war in this respect are very strict and have been and will continue to be fully enforced by me, but in any case the civil law gives full protection and specific complaints made either to me or the civil police will be fully investigated and dealt with.

I would, however, add that in several of the cases that have come to my knowledge and been investigated, the Italians have found all too ready co-operation from some of the local women, which of course, encourages them in this respect."

LETTERS OF THANKS

On December 15, 1947, the Mayor of Wells announced that the Penleigh Camp would shortly be vacated by its German prisoners.

Several letters of thanks were received by Somerset newspapers from POWs who were held in the Wells area. One prisoner, Hans-Georg Moschallski from Essen-Werden in Germany, who was held at Penleigh Camp, wrote to the *Wells Journal*, thanking the people of Mid Somerset for their kindness during his imposed stay.

"We were stationed in Nissen huts, about 30 or 40 men, I am not sure. On cold days it was the greatest problem to get the huts warm, coke was rare. There was no wood to start the fire. With old newspapers and cartons, we had some experts who managed to get over the problem."

Hans-Georg spent some time cleaning out the rivers around Wells. He said:

> *"It also belonged to my duties to visit, with the first lieutenant, sometimes with the chief of the camp Major Wightwick, ten farms daily, mostly dairy farms, where my fellow prisoners lived and worked. I am one of a very few POWs who knows Somerset very well, as 120 farms had to be visited. On these occasions I had the chance to be in contact with normal people.*
>
> *Our boys, my fellow prisoners, got on well with the farmers. From both sides we rarely heard complaints. Most were founded on language difficulties or misunderstandings. Besides discussions with them I had to arrange their change of clothes and to hand over three cigarettes for a day. It would be a crime to complain about POW time."*

He continued:

> *"Recollecting the memories of my captivity, I met so many friendly people at that time and feel that it is my duty to say thank you to all known and unknown people of Somerset.*
>
> *At Christmas 1946 we were all allowed to attend a church service, so we were marched, 10 to 20 men, to the Roman Catholic church in Wells. I remember there was a song during the service with a melody like our National Anthem and we sang our text.*
>
> *Before Christmas we were asked, or invited, to sing Christmas songs. About twenty men went to the organ gallery and, as I played the piano a bit, I was allowed to play the organ and after Mass we sang four or five Christmas carols. No one left the church and we began to sing Silent Night, the English joined us."*

Long after the war, Heinz Dietrich, who had been a Luftwaffe sergeant, arrived in Wells on holiday. He had first come to the area on May 7, 1941 when he was captured by the Home Guard after his Heinkel bomber was shot down near Langford. This time, he brought his wife with him to show her where his war had come to an end.

LASTING FRIENDS

For young brothers Jim and Edward Hanwell growing up at Cross Farm, Draycott, near Wells, the arrival of German POWs to work on the dairy and strawberry farm added extra interest to their lives.

The whole family took Hans Kahl and Paul Riwalsky to their hearts, and 60 years later the brothers were still in close touch with both Hans and Paul. Jim and Edward often spent holidays in Germany with the ex-prisoners; and their mother, Doris, was godmother to Hans Kahl's children.

A POACHER TURNS GAMEKEEPER

One particular German ex-prisoner of war Arnold Smolarczk hit the headlines in August 1984 when he became a security guard at the same spot where he was once held in captivity.

Arnold, a German tank driver, was first sent on the Russian campaign but was diverted to Paris, France. Sadly his brother continued to the Russian front where he was killed. In 1944 Arnold's tank broke down in action in Normandy at the battle of Falaise Gap, where he was captured.

As a POW Arnold was first sent to America, but 18 months later was sent to the UK. He remembers arriving at Maesbury Railway Station, and being marched up the road to the POW camp, which is now the Rocky Mountain Garden Centre.

Arnold Arnold (centre) with the security team on the day of his retirement   © *EMI Electronics Ltd*

Recalling his days as a POW, Arnold said:

> *"We were well treated during our incarceration at Penleigh, and at Christmas 1946, were even allowed out unsupervised in Wells."*

Worried by the political turmoil that engulfed Europe after the war, Arnold did not return to his (now) East German home. He chose instead to settle in Wells, where he married a local girl, and changed his unpronounceable German surname to Arnold.

After working on several farms in the area, and at the Mendip Hospital in Wells, Arnold's last job before retirement was as a security guard at Penleigh for EMI where he had been a prisoner during the war.

Arnold commented:

> *"I have been here so long that I am almost a local."*

Chapter Two

... there were three options, Reading, Malmsbury or Wells – the latter was chosen

At the start of the 1930s life in Wells continued little changed from one year to the next. In London, Solomon Sagall, an entrepreneur, was setting up a company called Scophony Ltd to exploit the patents of his partner, the inventor, George William Walton.

Sagall must have been a competent businessman because in 1932 the electronics company Ferranti invested

Solomon Sagall and George William Walton

£3,500 in the company. And when Ferranti turned down an option to invest a further £10,000 in the company two years later, EKCO (Eric Kirkham Cole Ltd) replaced them as Scophony's main investor.

By 1939 the company was based in a large residential property, Thornwood Lodge, in Campden Hill W8. Behind its imposing façade, the interior had been converted into a series of laboratories with engineers engaged on the early stages of television development. The company believed that if home television was to be a reality, the size, definition and brightness of the pictures had to be significantly improved.

After several years of development work, the Scophony engineers and scientists were able to demonstrate the result of their endeavours at the Radiolympia Exhibition in 1938, where the 24" pictures for home viewing were the biggest and brightest on display.

SCOPHONY TWO FOOT SCREEN HOME RECEIVER

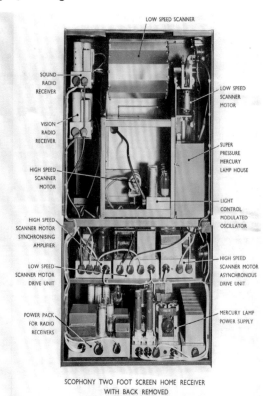

SCOPHONY TWO FOOT SCREEN HOME RECEIVER
WITH BACK REMOVED

Scophony's unique optical systems were outstanding technological achievements, enabling the company to become a leader in large-screen television development. Pictures taken by a Scophony television camera could be transmitted to various locations and the images viewed on a large screen, and in the late 1930s, they were the first company to transmit television pictures remotely to cinema screens.

The company did not limit itself to televisions for the home, but developed projectors and optics for much larger pictures, that it claimed could be watched by an audience of 500-700 people. These revolutionary projectors were intended for small cinemas, clubs and schools; and work on full cinema-screen television continued.

Then, as was the case with so many electronics companies, the outbreak of war changed everything.

As war with Germany became a reality, the focus of the engineering development at Scophony shifted to Ministry of Defence (MoD) work, and scientists, engineers and instrument-makers in the company were all obliged to sign the Official Secrets Act.

Scophony's expertise in televisions and projectors was redirected to military applications such as optical and mechanical instruments used in aircraft, sophisticated bombsights, and target-range measuring equipment. But events in London were starting to affect the work of the company.

Clem Clements had joined Scophony in February 1939 as a junior draughtsman. He takes up the story:

> *"One morning in 1940, we discovered that we couldn't go to work as a bomb was clearly visible in the red-shale tennis courts. Although it was eventually found to be an anti-aircraft shell, it caused a great deal of disruption, and some consternation.*
>
> *The government ministry now decreed that the work had to move out of London, and the company was offered three options; Reading, Malmsbury or Wells in Somerset. The latter was chosen.*

Opposite
above: *The two foot screen home receiver television illustrated in the 1938 Scophony Ltd brochure*
below: *Posters from the 1938 Radiolympia Exhibition*

Gustav Wickenhauser, a native Hungarian and a senior engineer at Scophony, was responsible for the move, and subsequently became the first General Manager at Wells. The workshops and stores were the first to move in October 1940, and were followed by the offices, including the drawing office where I worked, in November.

Various other personnel were transferred to Wells, and included a number of youngsters who had joined the company in 1940 to train as instrument-makers. Not all the London staff moved to Wells. Dr. Rosenthal, another senior electronics engineer, chose to move to America, together with some of his team."

Gustav Von Wikkenhauser, the first general manager at Wells

The skilled workforce that had moved down from London was quickly found places to live in and around Wells.

At this time there was very little industry in the city. Diploma Cheese, WCB Clares, Sheldon's Engineering (heavy machinery and foundry), and a paper mill, were about the extent of it. Unemployment was high, wages were low, and prospects for school-leavers were poor.

With the arrival of Scophony, many local people, mostly young women, were recruited to support the company in what was now priority war work, repairing and refurbishing equipment used in RAF and USAF aircraft. The company trained locals for assembly work, capstan lathe operation, work in the plating shop and the drawing office, general office duties, and planning and accounts.

A canteen for the Scophony workers was set up in the Crown Skittle Alley, and was open five days a week. A meal could also be had in the 'British Restaurant' at the Town Hall for about three shillings (15p).

Twice a day *Music While You Work*, broadcast on the BBC Home Service (now Radio 4), was relayed throughout the workshops, apparently to 'lessen strain, relieve monotony and thereby increase efficiency'.

Accommodating a new company like Scophony in Wells was not straightforward. Don Franklin joined the company soon after it came to Wells. He reports that a new

WCB Clares factory had just been built, but was empty, pending arrival of new printing machinery; it seems likely that the availability of this building was a key reason why Wells was one of the three listed locations. Compulsory building requisition orders were issued and Scophony moved in, bringing with them 'a bewildering array of apparatus'. In addition, several other locations were transformed into laboratories and workshops.

Wings for Victory week in Wells – a national fundraising scheme to raise money to purchase bomber planes, May 1943   © *Wells and Mendip Museum*

Town Hall buildings were also requisitioned, but were not large enough to take everything, so surplus stock was transferred to the Crump Way's cheese store, now the Co-operative supermarket's car park. Scophony's registered office and electronic laboratories found a new home at Tregantle, a large private house in Milton Lane.

Inevitably planning, production and quality control were all a little ad hoc to begin with, but the company soon found its feet in Wells and began to flourish. As demand increased a night shift was introduced, and at its peak Scophony employed about 400 people in Wells.

In the early years of the war, a kinetheodolite was captured from the enemy and it was passed on to Scophony. Scophony's task was to provide drawings of the device, to a suitable standard, so that more devices could be manufactured. This involved stripping down the kinetheodolite into all its constituent parts; and then producing a detailed drawing/specification for each of the parts.

Initially, the kinetheodolite was used as a training device, for improving the accuracy of artillery. The task of the operator was to get a target into view and keep it in view, i.e. to track the target.

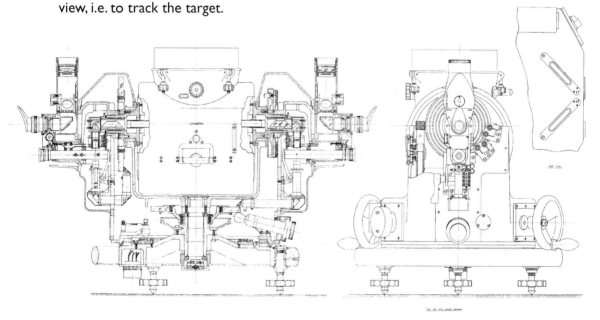

KINE - THEODOLITE, MARK II.
GENERAL ARRANGEMENT

Drawing of a kinetheodolite produced by 'Clem'

At that time the target in question was towed behind an aircraft and the artillery would attempt to hit the target. The various artillery explosions would be recorded. By carrying out this exercise using two kinetheodolites at known positions relative to each other, it was possible to collate the two recordings from the devices and calculate where in space and time the explosions took place, and their positions relative to the target. Recently, an original report showing drawings of the kinetheodolite, written in German, and dated 1936, was discovered among records at Thales in Wells.

Staff at Scophony worked on the renovation of airborne optical instruments and, because of Wikkenhauser's expertise, small special high-speed motors. Large quantities of the Switch Unit Type 35, used for aerial lobe and display switching in airborne radar, were manufactured. These units were needed in large numbers to equip aircraft, especially for night fighting.

The Switch Unit Type 35 production lines were soon supplemented by the manufacture of different types of motor-driven switches designed by Garrard's of Swindon.

As demand increased Scophony acquired more premises in Wells. The lens and ball-race polishing shops were transferred to Joe Thomas' scrap-metal yard in South Street. Although internally it was converted into laboratories, externally it still appeared to be little more than a scrap-yard. Here, specially-trained personnel worked on the repair of sophisticated military electronics equipment that had been war-damaged, and was awaiting urgent return to operational aircraft.

Clem Clements, who had come down to Wells with Scophony, joined the local platoon of the Home Guard headquartered at the Bishop's Barn. He talks of some of his more light-hearted experiences.

> *"During an exercise in a local quarry we practised throwing grenades. The platoon was lined up behind a bank, and told to lob their grenades well over the bank. The practice was certainly needed as at least one member launched his live grenade vertically. The assembled company moved back rather quickly; fortunately nobody was hurt.*
>
> *Later, the platoon was demonstrating its marching skills when a brass band started up on the bandstand. At first all was well, then an order was given that*

was half drowned by the noise of the band. Those at the front kept marching; those behind made a left turn, and those at the rear performed an about-turn. No one had heard of Dad's Army then."

A NEW HOME

After the war, many of the original London workforce opted to stay in the area, as did the company itself, and a hunt for suitable premises began. Wells City Council, anxious to attract light industry to the city, made plans to convert a cold store, which was owned by the council, to accommodate the company.

In 1948 George Conniford (left) was the first general manager for the Penleigh site and his son, Michael (right), was one of the first apprentices

However, at a meeting of the Wells City Council in March 1946, a delegate from the Trades Council pointed out that the building had been provided out of public funds, and should continue to be used for its original purpose as a central abattoir and cold storage. He commented:

> *"For the past eight months the building had been half empty, whereas now it could be fully utilised and would be capable of dealing with all the meat produced in the area."*

In response it was pointed out that a factory would produce considerably more jobs. Eventually, it was felt that the Trades Council could take no further action in the matter and the discussion was adjourned.

A great deal of time and energy was spent attempting to acquire suitable premises, without success. Finally, it was decided the only course of action was to erect a purpose-built building, and on 30th May 1947 a proposal was made to build a new factory, to be located on the site of the now vacant Penleigh prisoner-of-war camp on Wookey Hole Road. The *Wells Journal* commented:

> *"The new factory with its bungalow form, dull-red bricks, russet-brown roof, and windows will look far from factory-like.*

Aerial photo taken in the 1950s showing the new factory buildings © *English Heritage*

This is to be a pleasant place in which to work being light, air-conditioned, with an even temperature all the year round, and all the most up-to-date amenities. In these austere days only one thing is more difficult than building, and that is to build exactly the kind of building you want.

But Scophony is very much a key industry and they have reason to expect that they will move in at the end of the year to workshops which, if not quite perfect, will be the best the Government can allow.

Scophony's work is particularly suited to our countryside, for it is light, clean and very interesting. Commencing many years ago in London, as television research engineers, the company built up a reputation for inventing and high-precision instrument making which brought Government contracts for the design and production of air-defence equipment and such matters.

Scophony were pioneers in Radar, and their 'Skiatron' is an essential part of the equipment used by the United States Army All Weather Flying Centre, where it takes the place of the landing controller's eyes and memory, and enables them to land up to forty-five planes per hour.

For the industrial future of the country Scophony is developing motors of unique designs for the textile, timber and other trades which will speed up production far beyond the present capacity of plant, and it is for making these motors that a large area of the new factory will be used.

Development in the well-known Scophony system of television is far advanced and a new method of cinema film projection is nearing completion. Scophony instruments have a very important place in aircraft control and, even more important, in aircraft design research.

Many of such products are on the "secret list", and all that may be said of them is that their producers, the back-room boys of Wells, are among the foremost electronic designers in the country.

Incidentally, Scophony teams now have a county reputation for chess and table tennis, and fellow-citizens meet them on their Sports Ground at cricket, tennis and football. Meanwhile Scophony, with the aid of architects, building and other contractors, much advice from all quarters, and a great amount of official forms and correspondence, are building a new factory."

Everything was now in place to build the new factory – everything that is except the means to finance the project. An article that appeared in *The Times* in July 1948 and was also published in the *Wells Journal* made the following proposal:

"The 2,000 individual shareholders of Scophony Ltd., manufacturers of television and other apparatus will receive details of the board's plans for carrying on the business, together with the accounts for the past year. Under a reconstruction scheme submitted the 1,240,000 five shilling shares (25 new pence) are to be written down to one shilling (5p) each, and £160,000 of new money is to be sought.

The £248,000 cut in the capital is represented by £191,231 written off patents and development and by a net accumulated debit balance of £56,769. Holders of the 100 A Ordinary five shilling shares are asked to forgo their special rights, and in return holders of the Ordinary shares would transfer to them sufficient Ordinary to restore to A holders their existing rights. There would then be only one class of share.

If the scheme goes through the board intends issuing 2 million shares of 1 shilling each, 80% of which would be offered to present shareholders, and the balance taken up by the directors. This would provide £100,000 and another £60,000 would be raised by mortgage. The proceeds would be devoted as to £93,000 in financing the new factory, etc. and as to £67,000 for increasing stocks, providing working capital.

In support of the confidence they feel in the future, the directors report that since April 1st last, monthly production is over 50% up on the same period of the preceding year, and that big economies have been affected.

The accounts for the year ended March 31st last, show a loss of £33,215 against one of £41,818 for 1946-47; but the new board, which took over late in 1947, point out that two-thirds of last year's loss was incurred in the first six months of that year so that they halved the rate of loss.

If the scheme is carried through without delay the board are of the opinion that the trading result this year should not be unsatisfactory. While present output is necessarily confined to fractional motors and scientific instruments, plans are in hand for an extension of the present range of products, with special regard to exports and for television manufacture."

Early radar operator

The share launch was a success, and work on the new factory began at the Penleigh site on the Wookey Hole Road.

The company continued with its research and development work for the MoD, at the same time returning to the commercial world of television.

A STRATEGIC ALLIANCE

In 1947 Scophony Ltd merged with W. Andrew Bryce Ltd. and John Logie Baird Ltd. to form Scophony-Baird Ltd.

This was a significant moment as Baird, the inventor of the first publicly demonstrated television system, was the world leader in the continuing development and transmission of television. In 1941, Baird had patented, and demonstrated, a system of three-dimensional television; and in August 1944, he gave the world's first demonstration of a fully electronic colour television display.

By early 1949 the new factory on the Penleigh site was complete, and in April the *Wells Journal* was reporting on an official visit by the Mayor of Wells and other city councillors to the new Scophony-Baird works.

The visit, led by the Mayor Alderman E. E. Sheldon and members of the Wells City Council, took place on 6th April 1949.

The party split into four groups led by acting general manager C. J. Hyde-Trutch, works manager H. F. Clarke, technical sales manager P. L. F. Jones, and electronics section manager J. H. Townsend. They made a tour of the various departments where ranges of company's products were displayed.

A tea was laid on in the works canteen at which Hyde-Trutch expressed his appreciation on behalf of the company for the interest displayed by the city, and apologised for the unavoidable absence of S. Seeman, Scophony Baird's managing director.

Before tea, R. E. Duggan and Townsend demonstrated the company's latest product, the Soundmaster. This consisted of a magnetic tape recording attachment for home cinematograph projectors, which allowed home enthusiasts to record a running commentary on their (silent) films.

A major feature of the equipment was the ease with which the recorded material could be erased and replaced by fresh recordings, a revolutionary development in recording and replaying sound. The members of the council who tried their hand at recording their voices all expressed their surprise at the quality of the reproduction.

The *Wells Journal* wrote:

> *"As residents of the City know, Messrs. Scophony were evacuated to Wells from London during the early war-time blitz as they were the originators, and only*

manufacturers of an important part of the radar equipment so successfully used in hunting enemy submarines in the Atlantic.

The Company's reputation led to their being called upon to undertake other essential development and manufacture for the Government, and rapidly led to the premises allotted to them becoming too small, necessitating the acquisition of several outlying establishments.

After the close of hostilities it was decided that Wells being so suitable for their type of manufacture, a permanent home should be made there. The land comprising the Penleigh Camp was acquired and the present buildings erected with the active help of the City Council who had also been instrumental in causing the Company to come to its decision to remain in the area.

Following the Company's taking over of Messrs. John Logie-Baird, Ltd., and Messrs. W. Andrew Bryce Ltd., expansion of the Wells Works is proceeding actively, the only bar to continued progress being the lack of adequate facilities to house the Company's key personnel.

Operative labour of a high quality is available in the district, but for efficient employment requires the maintenance of a suitable balance of skilled personnel, much of which has to be imported into the district. It is hoped that, with adequate facilities in this direction, a doubling of the present number employed can be achieved in the not too distant future".

Scophony Baird Ltd. had by now clearly established itself as an important and valued part of both the economic and social life of the City of Wells.

CHAPTER THREE

'small fish in a large pond...'

At the end of the 1940s Scophony-Baird stood at a bleak crossroads. With the end of hostilities came the end of many of Scophony-Baird's lucrative MoD contracts, and though the company had successfully raised the capital necessary to build the new factory on the site at Penleigh, by 1950 it found itself in serious financial difficulties. To make matters worse, once the war had ended several key employees had left to return to London. There was a very real fear in the city that the site would close down completely with a disastrous effect on jobs in the area, and the local economy.

A much larger company, EMI (Electrical and Musical Industries), had been supplying components to Scophony-Baird Ltd. EMI realised what a unique group of scientists and engineers the company had assembled in Wells, supported by a skilled local workforce. At the end of 1950 EMI, which had its head office in Hayes, Middlesex agreed to take over Scophony-Baird and by February 1951 the sale was completed.

Scophony-Baird and its workforce now became part of EMI Engineering and Development, a division that the company had formed in 1945 specifically to undertake electronics-based projects.

Engineering and Development had already established a laboratory and workshop at Feltham, Middlesex; and in 1951 as well as the Scophony-Baird operation in Wells, it took over a large works at Treorchy in South Wales.

EMI swiftly announced a cash injection of £250,000 (£2 million in today's money) for the Wells site, and arranged for several of its existing contracts to be transferred to Penleigh. The threat of major redundancies was averted, and the future of the Penleigh Works now seemed secure.

A NEW ERA

The EMI takeover produced a fundamental shift in the character of the Penleigh Works. Up to this point Scophony-Baird had operated as a small independent company. Masters of their own destiny, they could choose the direction the company was to take, and the products it would produce. Now the workforce and management found themselves a small part of a large international organisation with diverse interests around the world.

By the start of the 1950s EMI was already a household name in the UK. It was also a major player on the world stage with a well-established portfolio of business interests in television, radio, electronics, and the music and film industries. It was also involved in a number of defence projects including the development of ground and airborne radar systems.

Although the company was just 20 years old in 1951, its pedigree stretched back to the late 19th century with The Gramophone Company, HMV (His Master's Voice), and the Columbia Gramophone Company, which between them formed EMI in 1931.

Scophony-Baird had been a big fish in what was a small pond; the takeover by EMI left the workforce and management at Penleigh a much smaller fish (albeit a more secure one) in a very much larger pond.

EMI MOVES IN

EMI's plan for Wells was to establish an operation that could undertake Research and Development (R&D); high quality electronic engineering; and small-run manufacturing of complex electronic products. The range of buildings at Penleigh fitted EMI's needs perfectly. Furthermore, the 'rural' setting in the Somerset countryside, and the proximity to the tranquil city of Wells, were definite selling points when it came to attracting specialised engineers, scientists and senior management.

Gradually, the prison huts that had been converted for Scophony-Baird were demolished and new buildings replaced them. These included a main office/admin block, a machine shop, and several large single-storey workshops for electronic assembly, inspection and testing. The new buildings were fully equipped for modern precision engineering, and complex electro-mechanical research, design, manufacture and prototype assembly.

Penleigh site in the 1950s

Building work in the 1950s

Building work in the 1950s. Note the Prisoner-of-War hut inside

APPRENTICESHIPS

One definite bonus that came with the EMI takeover was the introduction of the company's apprenticeship schemes to Wells; a scheme that had been running successfully at the Hayes site ever since it was introduced there in 1945. Stan Blackmore and Ron Wallis, pictured below, were responsible for the training and development of a large number of apprentices over many years.

Wells Apprentice Sports Team, taken at Hayes in 1960

Back row left to right: Stan Blackmore, Ian Clements, Ed Brown, Mick Sugden, Stan Carpenter, Trevor Mitchell, Alan Tilley, Fred Townsend, Ron Wallis

Front row left to right: Roy Moon, Martin Lambert, Adrian Morgan, Pete Bakey, Wally Foster

1961 Apprentices

Back Row: George Tilley, Roy Windsor, Peter Oliver, Melvyn Hill, Paul Hucker

Front Row: David Swift, Malcolm Stephens, John Tarran, Charles Farmer

1962 Apprentices

Back Row: R. Tibbs, B. Over, P. Parkman, A. Stock, K. Plummer, A. Ashman, A. Eddolls, R. Whitacre, J.M. Saleer

Front Row: P. Dessi, C. Pickthall, J. Farrow, A. Cousins, R. Oatley, M. Selway

1963 Apprentices

Back Row: Peter Butler, John Puddy, Alan Gumbleton, Alan Comer, Philip Kerton, Kenneth Matthews

Front Row: Richard Harris, Leslie Perrett, Robert Bailey, Robert Sherriff, Paul Elvin, Philip Weston

1964 Apprentices

Back Row: Keith Rogers,
Philip Green, Richard Webb,
Michael Cox,
Geoffrey Latham,
Martin Rumary,
James Loynd

Front Row: Robert Berman,
Anthony Perrett,
Graham Govier,
Gerald Payne,
Bernard Robbins,
Stephen Pople,
Gregory Villis

1965 Apprentices

Back Row: David Gill, Nigel Cripps,
David Weeks, Ian Horler,
Brian Chandler, Michael Ross,
Ronald England

Front Row: Antony Musgrave,
Ian Mill, Reevley Stephens,
Alan Corlet, Raymond Morgan,
David Fisher, Richard Hole

1966 Apprentices

Back Row: Peter Griggs,
Christopher Leney, Richard Moon,
Michael Abbott, David Crowcombe,
James Coles, Richard Harris

Front Row: Ernest Parfitt,
Keith Boulter, Michael Dark,
Roger Coombes, Alan Ellaway,
Trevor Haskins

Inset: Philip Chambers,
David Westcott,
Peter Vancuylenburg

1967 Apprentices

Back Row: Jones,
Haynes, Latty,
Carpenter,
Hawkes-Pippen,
Smith, Lamb,
Stewart

Front Row: Dessi,
Higginson, Elms,
Dalwood, Hathway,
Durston

Inset:
David Cluttterbuck

1968 Apprentices

Back Row: D. Major, P. Thomas,
P. Spencer, E. Cripps

Front Row: N. Dury, A. Hawkins, P. Cooper

1969 Apprentices

Back Row: A. Cook,
R. Cholmondeley,
T.C. Chivers, G.I. Jones,
T.J. Plumley

Front Row: P.W. Young,
J.W. Hughes,
M.J. Slocombe, T.J. Ellaway,
R.N. Gulliford, M. Evans

1970 Apprentices

Back Row: D.M. Swain, F.J.A. Delaney, J.E. Buckley, S.G. Tungate, D.L.J. Pullen

Front Row: J.S. Roberts, L.S. Daniels, A.K. Bennett, M.D. Sims

1971 Apprentices

Back Row: C. Jenkins, R. O'Meara, R.C. Harris, P. Ware

Front Row: A. Bazell, R.P. Harris, B. Messenger, S. Jackson

1972 Apprentices

Back Row: R. Symes, G. Maggs, R. Lacy, I. Miles

Front Row: G. Warwick, H. Stone, P. Thomas, K. Tuck

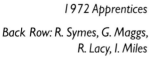

1973 Apprentices

Back Row: A. Dymond, M. Roberts, A. Watson, I. Stitch, S. Carpenter

Front Row: J. Smith, C. Palmer, M. Raynor, A. Bennett, L. Gaulton

1974 Apprentices

Back Row: P. Payne, M. Wills, N. Newton, N. Tarrant, N. Clark, A. Roper

Front Row: M. Wigglesworth, R. Maltby, D. Urch, J. Bobbett, S. Flood, J. Prideaux

1975 Apprentices

From left to right: Tony Fricker, Mike Pollard, Brian Workman, Mike Jackson, Dave Chorley, Graham Lukins, Andrew Woolley, Paul Hughes, Martin Rivers, Roger Jones, Nick Milbourne

1976 Apprentices

Back Row: Robert Smart, Kerry Dyer, Jon Hutton, Timothy Taylor, Anthony Wood

Front Row: John Alford, Ian Hooper, James Nash, Derick Bond, Andrew Harris

1977 Apprentices

Back Row: Ian Crighton, Ross Baker, John Millbank, Ashley Hardwell, Ian Howard, Robin Radford

Front Row: Richard Webber, Leslie Wills, Keith Meadon, Hazel Bailey, Christopher Sperring

Under the scheme, craft apprenticeships were available to applicants who had a secondary education to CSE level; and Technician apprenticeships were offered to applicants who had GCE O level passes in four subjects, including mathematics, physics and English. Applicants with good grades at GCE A level in physics and mathematics could apply for an undergraduate apprenticeship that led to a 'sandwich' degree in electrical and electronic engineering.

The scheme was so popular with local school leavers that it was common for the company to receive up to 100 applications for the 12 places available each year.

MEMORIES OF EMI – A 60s APPRENTICESHIP

Bernie Mundy remembers:

"It was a different world when I joined the company in 1966. Hendrix and the Beatles were in their prime and a whole generation was finding its feet after the fairly strict post-war years that their parents had endured. Long hair, jeans and T-shirts were not the ubiquitous uniform they are now, and work colleagues frowned on those that did not match the perceived sartorial elegance of the 50s and 60s workplace. Throw a disparate bunch of teenagers into the mix and truly the times they were a changin'. I joined a wonderful bunch of young apprentices when I joined the company, but rather than the traditional 'skills' apprenticeship, I was pioneering (or a guinea pig more like) a new idea where instead of focusing on workshop ability I worked in a variety of departments from Planning and Stock Control through to the management of a research and development group under the watchful eye of the doleful George Martin.

There were some memorable personages in that specific year's intake, Richard Moon and Dave Crowcombe, to name but two. However, in this Zeitgeist of burgeoning revolution it was one fellow I remember above all others, and for the sake of decorum I will not name him fully but only as Steve.

During coffee breaks and the like Steve and myself became obsessed with the idea of forming an escape committee of apprentices so that we too could join the ever expanding army of the newly liberated youth. The plan went as far as to design sweatshirts that demonstrated this desire, and it was an open secret when they were finally manufactured and delivered, and about 50 arrived on site for sale and distribution. There, boldly emblazoned on these royal blue sweatshirts was the tag 'EMI Escape Committee'.

All went very well until everyone wore them to work on the same day. The management was not pleased. Looking back am I surprised - NO!

Both Steve and myself were questioned, and owned up to being the protagonists of the joke. Well you did in those days. Suitably chastened the sweatshirts were abandoned from the workplace, and if anything like my own stored for future reflection. Somewhere in the attic is one of these iconic items of clothing.

I almost forgot about this whole episode until nearly 30 years later my daughter, then living in Bristol, said that she had met an old colleague of mine, who when he realised who she was (recognising the surname) reminded her that in our youth we had been a couple of pranksters! Of course it was Steve - now a member of the establishment bringing up his own family.

Like I said it was a different world back then."

DEFENCE WORK

When EMI took over Penleigh, work initially focussed on design and manufacture for new defence projects including electronics for guided missiles, telemetry, underwater detection, and armed services training equipment. The company brought with it several existing defence projects including telemetry devices for use in guided missiles, and tactical trainers, the first of a range of simulators that allowed personnel to be trained without the costly use of ships, aircraft or missiles.

DEVELOPMENT OF RADAR

EMI and Scophony-Baird shared a common expertise in the development of the technologies (e.g. high-frequency pulses and cathode-ray tubes) used in both television and radar. Consequently, it was natural that the Wells division would become involved in the development of radar, which EMI had been developing since before the war.

Among the first radar-based technologies that EMI had developed during the war was a 'blind-bombing' radar system code-named H2S. The project was led by one of EMI's most brilliant engineers, A. D. Blumlein, who tragically lost his life when a Halifax bomber crashed during early trials of the equipment in 1942. However, work went on, and the H2S radar system became a vital tool in the Pathfinder 1000-bomber raids on Germany.

Peacetime development of the H2S was to form an early part of the work undertaken by the new team at Wells, and in 1951, the EMI management transferred some development work on the H2S Mk.1XA, a radar altimeter and sextant used as a radar bombing aid, to Wells. This was a significant moment as it represented the first step in bringing EMI's military work to Wells, albeit work that was largely managed from Feltham.

By 1953, H2S Mk.1XA work was well established, and Wells was beginning to win work with its own competitive tendering, enabling the Penleigh site to pursue a more independent course.

Alongside the defence projects, work at Wells during this period included the design and manufacture of industrial tape recorders, closed-circuit television systems, picture monitors for the BBC and ITV, and instruments for analysing and measuring nuclear contamination.

RADAR PROXIMITY FUZING

Many of the technologies that the Penleigh team developed ran like threads through the various changes of ownership and management of the site at Wells. One particular project that demonstrates this remarkable continuity relates to radar proximity fuzes, an activity that lay hidden under a security blanket for many years.

For a munition to be triggered to explode at an appropriate moment, typically when it is close to its intended target, it requires a device for detecting the presence of the target and then initiating the explosion. Such devices are known as proximity fuzes and EMI had been heavily involved with radar fuzes for anti-aircraft shells during World War II; in the early 1950s this work continued but for air-to-air guided missiles.

With the advent of the Cold War this work had to be moved away from London to avoid covert surveillance from foreign aircraft. Eventually the Wells factory was acquired by EMI Electronics and in so doing, satisfied the need for EMI to provide a location remote from foreign surveillance.

Initially its new site was used for telemetry work for guided weapons trials activities at Feltham. Then, in December 1954 a Special Projects laboratory was set up, under Ron Crook, for work on radar fuze research projects. Initial projects the laboratory undertook, included work on the ground-approach fuze that involved making a radar, installing it in a Valetta aircraft and recording the radar reflection coefficients of the ground when flying over various terrains. The flights were made from RAF Locking, near Weston-super-Mare, where the aircraft was permanently stationed, and kept available for the fuzing team to use.

PRANGER

In May 1956 Bill Gilmour (then head of fuzing at Wells) and Brian Jackson (his deputy) were called in to help EMI Feltham with some fuze production problems.

On the way home from the meeting Bill and Brian decided that a new approach was needed, and during the journey they devised a new Pulse Range Gate system to replace a system that was failing. The following day a patent was applied for in the UK (and later in the USA) and the system named Pranger.

Two weeks later Brian demonstrated to the MoD using a bow and arrow. The radar, operating at a frequency in the X-band, was placed on the ground, looking upwards. Arrows, covered in tinfoil patches, were shot into the air with a bow. When an arrow passed close to the radar, it set off a bell. It worked!

Proving tests needed to be carried out on weapons more sophisticated than bows and arrows, and the team set about making realistic prototypes for Seaslug, Bloodhound and Thunderbird ground-to-air missiles.

The new systems used radar pulses as opposed to the Feltham continuous wave, frequency modulated (FM) design. The MoD cancelled the contract for the FM fuzes but awarded EMI contracts to develop Pranger fuzes for Seaslug, Bloodhound and Thunderbird, and later for other missiles, a very significant set of contracts for the company and the team at Wells.

RADIO MODELLING

The MoD soon became very interested in the capabilities of the system. In late 1956 they approached Wells, and asked if a sub-scale model of the Pranger system could be developed using a new 70GHz Magnetron as source of the model radar's radiation. This was roughly seven times higher in frequency than used by full-scale Pranger, and meant that fuzing scenarios could be modelled at roughly one-seventh scale.

Brian and his colleague, Len Cram, scoured Somerset looking for a suitable location for carrying out modelling exercises. They eventually settled on Weston Hangar at Locking where the RAF kept their Valetta – thus Radio Modelling was born. Once the modelling facility was up and running, the validity of the modelling work was confirmed by full-scale trials carried out at Westbury Beacon.

The principle of modelling radar systems could be applied to many radar applications, not just fuzing radars, and there have been many subsequent developments. For example, in order to model ships, a scale factor of about one seventh would not

An RAF Canberra appears over Westbury Beacon for low-level radar tests

do – a ship modelled at that scale wouldn't even fit in the hangar. The requirement to model ships spawned another field of research at Wells; Laser Technology. Brian Prewer and Peter Short developed radar systems working at 890GHz a scale factor for the models of approximately one ninetieth – which was a feasible scale for making ship models.

MoD contracts for radio fuzing and radio modelling work were a mainstay of the Wells site over the course of its life. In order to carry out the work a large team was set up, and significant infrastructure was developed on-site including a purchasing department, information services and security, alongside the various manufacturing facilities. Eventually, the department achieved much acclaim for its work on radar signatures and stealth for aircraft, tanks and ships, and was heavily involved during the Falklands War.

The modelling department still exists, having moved to Templecombe following the closure of the Penleigh site, and we shall return to the modelling teams and their work in Chapter Four.

CHANGES AT THE TOP

In 1955 J. F. Lockwood (later Sir Joseph) became chairman of EMI Limited, and immediately made changes to the company's corporate structure. He felt that the various electronics operations within EMI needed streamlining, and did so by amalgamating them into a single new company, EMI Electronics Limited. C. Metcalfe (later CBE) was appointed managing director and EMI operation at Wells became a part of the new company.

P. A. Allaway (later Dr. Allaway, CBE) succeeded Metcalfe as managing director in 1961. He continued to expand electronics activities, and was instrumental in the extension of the buildings at Wells. In 1965, Viscount Mills, KBE, Chairman of the EMI Group, opened the new buildings in the presence of the Mayor of Wells, H. Teagle, city councillors, and other local dignitaries.

Percy Allaway, (right) Managing Director

Soon after his appointment, Allaway's assessment of the future direction for the whole EMI defence effort was delivered to the Chairman of the EMI Group of Companies, Lord Mills. Taking into account the situation that then existed at Hayes, Feltham and Wells, Allaway proposed that a new divisional structure be implemented. His recommendation was accepted, and from 1966 onwards, the structure was progressively applied.

This was the first of many re-organisations of the EMI Group as the senior management struggled throughout the 1960s to make sense of the increasingly diverse collection of businesses that they owned.

In spite of the turmoil at the head office in Hayes, EMI Wells continued to deliver significant breakthroughs in electronics throughout the 60s and 70s including the Electroscan, the T3 Hand-held Digital Radar Gun, and the EMI 8800 Superdrive.

THE ELECTROSCAN

Towards the end of the 1950s, largely as a result of a merger in another part of its business, EMI acquired PET (Precision Electrical Terminations), a company based in Sevenoaks. The company was run by Lee Kemp, who suggested to his new bosses at EMI that PET should diversify its interest into marine instrumentation.

Under a new company to be known as EMI Marine, Kemp proposed that PET should begin the design, manufacture and sale of a range of navigation aids aimed at the growing leisure boating market. These instruments would measure depth of water, boat speed, distance travelled and wind direction, in addition to maintenance and advisory services. The company was duly formed in 1958 with Kemp as its General Manager in Sevenoaks.

In 1967 the company turned its attention to the potential addition to its range of a small-boat radar system suitable for sea-going cruisers. This was an area where several companies had already been successful and the EMI Board gave approval for the project.

Sea trials of a prototype were successfully completed by 1968, and production of the radar system, known as 'Electroscan', began at Wells. The first sets went on sale in 1969, initial sales were encouraging, and the set performed well. Great attention had been paid to the styling and general appearance of the Electroscan, and the prestige of having one on the masthead of your cruiser was thought to be a major factor in its appeal.

During 1970, a number of service failures occurred with installed Electroscan units. Under normal circumstances these would have been dealt with locally, and cause little problem. However, luxury cruisers were often in inconveniently exotic locations when the equipment failed, and the cost of maintaining them under warranty became an increasingly heavy burden.

After a review in 1972, production and sales of the unit were dropped. In the general reshuffle later in 1972 the EMI Marine Division was wound up, and with it EMI's connection with commercial marine surface radar.

THE T3 HAND-HELD DIGITAL RADAR GUN

Of the many products developed by EMI Wells during this period one in particular stands out, but not always for positive reasons – the so-called portable digital radar gun (speed gun).

Gordon Selby and Alan Cuff demonstrating the original prototype hand-held digital radar gun

Alan Cuff, now a senior software engineer, was involved in the trials of the hand-held unit that was based on a product EMI had bought from a Canadian company. Talking about the early days of the speed gun Alan remembers:

"My colleague, Gordon Selby, was often called as an expert witness in court cases. His job was to verify or disprove claims made by drivers who had been prosecuted for speeding offences on the basis of the measurements provided by the device. To produce results for these court cases I worked with Gordon, driving his car at various locations to test the findings.

Claims we investigated included:

A radio transmitter interfered with the radar gun – disproved by driving several times up and down past the Charterhouse police transmitter station.

I was driving through a large puddle which affected the radar gun – disproved by driving back and forth through puddles of various depths near Priddy.

There were several parked cars that interfered with the radar gun – disproved by driving several times up and down Ash Lane in Wells past a series of parked cars.

I was driving past an industrial site with a long chain link fence – disproving by driving up and down Wookey Hole Road past the EMI factory.

Another trial involved a large display board on wheels; a radar speed gun was operated to send data as a number display so as to show the speed of oncoming vehicles to their drivers. Much fun was had when we tested it outside the factory on the main road (in those days the 30mph speed limit didn't begin until Ash Lane)."

Data recording equipment

SE LABORATORIES LIMITED

As part of its general policy of expansion, EMI continued acquiring other companies. One of these was SE Laboratories Limited, later renamed EMI Data Tech, a company specialising in complex measuring machines.

SE Laboratories (EMI) Ltd Wells 1979

Front Row left to right: Julie Bishop, Dick Nash, Pam James, Doug Miller, Ken Lunn, Dave McCormick, Bert Oram, Don Holly, Kevin Baker, Graeme Richards, Jack Harwood, Mike Perry, Alan Worrell, Norman Tooze, Pat Taylor, Ray Fowler, John Davis, Jim Darch, Steve Rea, Tony Richardson, Chris Dawkins, Rusty Farrell

Second Row left to right: Joyce Webb, Lil Jenkins, Vi Cribb, Phil Spacey, Sue Trippick, Denise Malyan, Stella Wood, Beryl Nicholls, Wendy Payne, Syvlia Rook, Netta D'Amor, Jenny Grenter, Sue Bradfield, Sandra Grimstead, Sharon Pointing, Mandy Thorpe, Nicky Dando, Maeve Holliday, Pam Shopland, Peter Wilkins, Walter Curtis, Fraser Nash, Charlie Watkins, Jim Cogswell, Ken Mounty

Third Row left to right: Ann Garland, Marian Rumley, Jenny Hancock, Margaret Greenall, Sue Davis, Caroline Plenty, Sybil Pearson, Molly Bennets, Pat Cutter, Win Baker, Ann Bradfield, Janet Stone, Margaret Flinders, Jackie Oatley, Pauline Edwards, Lynn Iveson, Carol Iveson, Lena Raso, Betty Loxton, Alice Atkins, Karen Arnold, Pam Whitcombe, Marion Rivers, Theresa Middleton

Fourth Row left to right: Ken Moxham, Trevor Wills, Derek Flood, Bob McNally, John Allen, Charlie Boardman, Brian Hooper, John (surname not known), Franco Berti, Mike Oram, Brenda Durnford, Pat Young, Carol Jones, Joan Moxey, Cherry Griffin, Maureen Palmer, Jean Matthews, Christine Wellen, Sandra Booker, Jean Jones, Joan Dudden, Janet Dibben, Dot O'Connell, Debbie Dando, Sue Burr

Fifth Row left to right: George Govier, Alan Goodliffe, Ron Norton, Frank Gooding, Martin Payne, Derek Greenman, Ray Hodges, Albert George, Mark House, Rob Durnford, Jeremy Richards, Pat Curtis, Sheila Townsend, Roy Hawksworth, George Varney, Margaret Varney, Alison Crook, Tony Thompson, Alan Redman, Terry Dukes, Phil Coles, Brian Sutton, Arthur Perry, John O'Connell

Sixth Row left to right: Jim Iveson, George Jones, Idris Hemmins, Chris Heal, Dave Colburn, Tim Haskins, Rob Whitcombe, Chris George, Ted Iveson, Fred Peek, Chris Jennings, Dave Clark, Richard Jones, Ray Jelly, Derek Lukins, Simon Bankes, Steve Zadeh (Shah Jenson), Kevin Fisher, Alan Bailey, Gresham Deverill, Chris Oliver, Tony Poyntz, Ray Cook, Chris Brooks

Back Row left to right: Pete Wellen, Dennis Middleton, John Sadler, Colin Powell, John Doyle

SE/EMI Data Tech produced a vast range of instruments including oscilloscopes, timer counters, frequency response analysers, magnetic tape recorders, UV (Ultra Violet) chart recorders, pressure transducers, and strain measurement systems. They set up an operation at the Penleigh site to develop magnetic recording technology, and in 1979 announced the EMI 8800 digital tape transport.

THE EMI 8800 SUPERDRIVE

The EMI 8800, given the name Superdrive, was similar to a large tape recorder. It drove the magnetic tapes that early computers used to store vast quantities of data such as detailed bank records.

With the machine designed in a modular system, if anything went wrong the faulty part could easily be removed and replaced. The EMI 8800 also contained its own mini-computer capable of detecting faults immediately, and the time for carrying out repairs averaged less than 40 minutes.

The Superdrive was the result of over two years of research at the Penleigh laboratories, and EMI Data Tech were quick to claim it as a major breakthrough in a market dominated by the American giants.

Dr. Duke Ebenezer, head of the Wells design team, went to the Hanover International Trade Fair to launch Superdrive in May 1979. He said at the time:

> *"It immediately attracted interest, not only from companies in Western Europe but from the Americans and East Europeans as well. It's a winner.*

> *Too often British ingenuity has resulted in major technological breakthroughs which have then been snapped up by the giant American companies who have concentrated their efforts not into research, but into marketing. We make the discoveries, but they make the money.*

> *So when we started the design work we set out to discover exactly what the market wanted. We looked at existing machines and decided to design something better.*

> *The EMI 8800 is cheaper to buy, run and service; it's much easier to repair and it even looks better than anything else on the market."*

25 YEARS AT PENLEIGH

In 1976 EMI Electronics Wells celebrated its Silver Jubilee with an exhibition held on three floors of the Town Hall in the Market Place. Members of Penleigh staff manned the exhibition stands, happy to answer any questions put by the public.

Company products displayed ranged from tiny components used in circuits operating at microwave frequencies to much larger equipment such as the ill-fated EMI Scanner (see Chapter Four), then the very latest development in X-ray technology.

Alongside contemporary products, examples of earlier products were exhibited. These included a closed-circuit television that was used on flight trials of the prototype of Concorde and many examples of the company's research and development work.

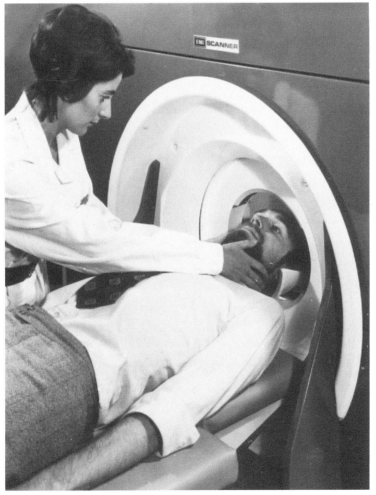

EMI Scanner

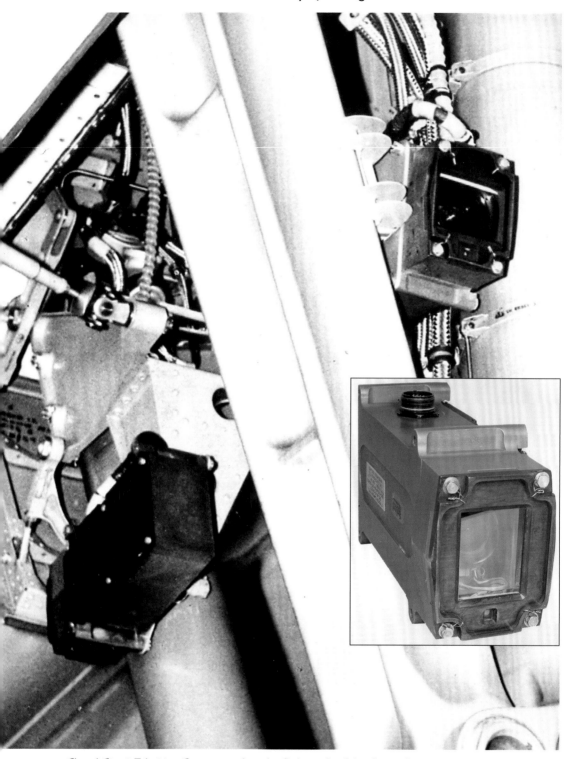

Closed Circuit Television Camera used on the flight trials of the Concorde prototype

Visitors could see a computer terminal in action (remember this was 1976), and there were film and slide demonstrations, including one showing the latest technique of precision cutting of micro-circuits by laser. EMI Wells Service and Maintenance department was also well represented, with displays showing their contribution to activities at the Penleigh site.

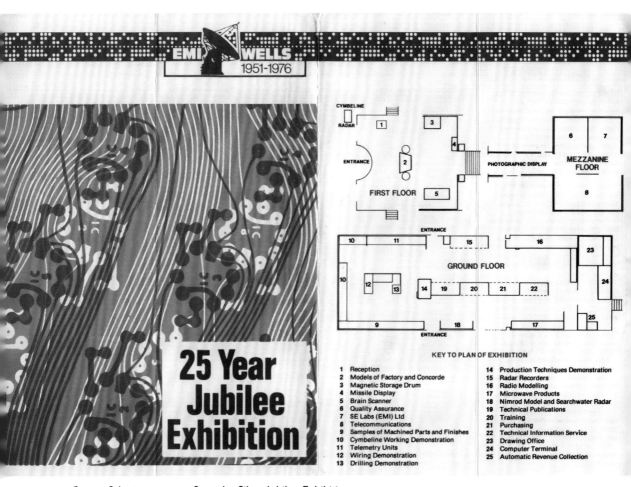

Cover of the programme from the Silver Jubilee Exhibition

STORM CLOUDS GATHER

Three years later, in April 1979, EMI Electronics was celebrating record order books, but in presenting the results for the previous half year, the board ominously warned that the outlook for the group as a whole in the second half of the financial year continued to be uncertain.

EMI had been thriving on the massive boom in British pop music record sales both at home and abroad – The Beatles were just one of the phenomenal successes of its many recording artists. Two brothers, Lew Grade and Bernard Delfont, who had already built a huge showbusiness and entertainment empire, now spearheaded the company's success.

Delfont, Grade and many EMI shareholders were convinced that the success of the company was being driven by the healthy profits and generous margins that the entertainment divisions of EMI were delivering. They were far less enamoured of the hard-to-quantify, sometime non-existent, profits that electronic technology, especially research and development, was generating for the company's balance sheet.

Research engineers and scientists at Wells now found themselves working for a company that owned glamorous assets such as Elstree Studios, The London Palladium, Blackpool Tower and ATV (Associated Television), but seemed to have little interest in pioneering electronic design.

In spite of the somewhat negative attitude of the group's senior management, EMI Electronics Ltd announced that it was to double the apprentice intake over the following five years. In the previous year the company had received a staggering 150 applications for the 12 apprenticeships on offer at Wells.

Dr. Allaway, chairman of EMI Electronics, explained why the expansion plan, although good news, would not be easy:

> "We will have to spend money on extending training facilities; find more training places in our workshops, drawing offices and laboratories. We shall have to prepare more experienced staff for supervision of training in these places.
>
> Above all we shall have to be looking at the detail of our training to see that it is preparing young people for the needs of future years, and that we are not training them to suit yesterday's technology.
>
> We are known for our close relationship with educationalists at every level, but we shall have to look at other ways in which we can help, guide or influence, so as not only to help EMI but also, that the wider manufacturing industry can benefit in the long run.

At the moment most engineering companies in the manufacturing industry are concerned about the lack of skilled and experienced staff. We have been trying to look forward beyond some of the problems that world business has brought to EMI and we can see that the shortages of well trained and educated staff will not only persist but probably will get worse.

The effects of the falling birth rate will be affecting the numbers of school leavers making fewer available for apprenticeships and to go on to university. There will be the effects of the service industries drawing more staff from the manufacturing industry as technology gets absorbed into commercial activities."

The EMI apprentice scheme was a unique opportunity for young people in Wells and John Gibson describes his pride, and sense of achievement at having been selected as an apprentice at EMI in 1960:

"It was quite a thing to be at EMI. Part of this I think was the prestige ascribed by people outside EMI, seeing the works security patrolling the perimeter and hearing of the mystery of electronics.

Of course some of the work going on there would be for a purpose, and going places that were subject to some secrecy and high security – all contributing to the mystique of the place.

But as an apprentice, the only thing you knew when you started was that you had to fill in a huge long application as to your family's political leanings, was your great, great grandfather a supporter of Italy's Garibaldi uprising and so on. You had the security; you had the mystique, and yet when you stepped through the security gates it was not at all what you expected, although men in their white coats, flitting silently around, did add to the air of mystery.

When I had completed my apprenticeship I was offered a job in the machine shop. I asked what the wage would be, and the manager asked me what figure I had in mind. I said, the going rate was twelve guineas per week – "We can't go that far" I was told, so we settled on eleven guineas, which tickled me, as guineas (£1.1s or £1.10p) had gone out of use long ago – but this was EMI after all!"

Machine shop

Throughout most of the 1960s, EMI Wells employed some 1000 people at Penleigh. Several of the workers, many of whom lived up to 20 miles away, travelled in by coach from Bristol, Weston-super-Mare and Norton-Radstock.

Now, in spite of Dr. Allaway's best intentions, events on the larger stage were once again to have a profound effect on the Penleigh Works. The number of employees started to fall dramatically as EMI struggled to find its way in a rapidly changing world.

MORE PHOTOS . . .

More construction

Building the boiler tower

*Ivy in Staff sales
– 1976*

*Jim Curtis photography
– 1976*

Mike Penery
(centre)
demonstrates a
prototype ticket
machine to the
Very Revd. Dean P.
Mitchell and Mrs.
W. Pinchery

Visits in the 1970s

Thorn EMI Ltd Racal Radar Defence Ltd
Thomson-CSF Thorn EMI Ltd Racal Radar
Defence Ltd Thorn EMI Ltd Racal Radar
Racal Radar Defence Ltd Thomson-CSF
Thorn EMI Ltd Racal Radar Defence Ltd
Thomson-CSF Thorn EMI Ltd Racal Radar

CHAPTER FOUR

'merger, restructure, restructure, restructure – sale, restructure – sale…'

MERGER

From 1978 EMI Electronics Ltd faced increasing serious financial difficulties. This was largely due to its infatuation with computed tomography scanning for medical diagnostics, i.e. the body scanner.

Rather than licensing the technology that it had developed, EMI made the mistake of creating a new medical division, complete with its own sales force, service structure, and R&D department, simply to service a single product, the body scanner.

To make matters worse, just as EMI made the final commitment to the project, both in the UK, and at their new American factory in Northbrook, Illinois, aggressive new American trade legislation effectively shut EMI out of their largest potential market for scanners.

For a while the EMI Group tried to replace this disastrous loss of revenue from the new medical division by transferring money from other more profitable operating divisions. By1980, however, it became clear that the situation could not be resolved from internal resources alone.

Under these difficult circumstances, discussions took place between Sir John Reed, Chairman of the EMI Group, and Sir Richard Cave, Chairman of Thorn Industries, to agree a merger. At the same time, the company was urgently seeking a buyer for its ailing medical division.

At the end of October 1979 EMI had rejected a £145 million bid by Thorn. The offer was resubmitted the following week for £165 million, and was accepted. The

EMI Group of Companies was merged with Thorn Industries, and the company's name was changed to Thorn EMI plc on March 3, 1980. The overall result of the merger was that effective control of the EMI Group passed to Thorn, which then held the majority of voting shares on the new board.

Initially it was a difficult relationship as the various divisions within the old Thorn and EMI organizations continued to operate independently of each other and, to some extent, of the central management group.

Management implemented a business model, developed by the Boston Consulting Group, that provided for the development of new enterprises by channelling funds from profitable operations. This had the effect of starving the successful enterprises within the company of funds needed to maintain competitive product lines.

In an attempt to raise money, and reduce losses, the company sold its medical electronics business, its hotels and restaurant division, and parts of the leisure and entertainment division.

RESTRUCTURE

Peter Laister, who had been managing director at Thorn and subsequently Thorn EMI, attempted to create a more efficient operation by acquiring new divisions, including Inmos, a microchip manufacturer which was acquired in 1984. Laister's strategy was to develop an integrated communications and entertainment business, with particular emphasis on advanced electronics.

Eventually the merger began to flourish; Thorn's investors who at first were opposed to the acquisition of EMI were soon applauding the move as new contracts, particularly for the electronics division, began to flow in.

SEARCHWATER

Almost immediately the team at Wells became involved in the Searchwater project.

Searchwater, originally a Thorn product, went into service with RAF Coastal Command in 1978. At that time it was the world's most powerful airborne radar for marine reconnaissance. From 1980, other uses of long-range airborne radar began to be examined, including adapting Searchwater to be fitted to naval helicopters such as the Westland Sea King.

By the beginning of 1982 an innovative design had been agreed which allowed the radar to be swung out and down when deployed, and retracted before landing. In the savage 1982 defence review the project was shelved, only to be resurrected weeks later, when Britain went to war with Argentina over the disputed ownership of the Falkland Islands.

The sinking of HMS Sheffield in the South Atlantic at the beginning of the war demonstrated the desperately urgent need for a sophisticated radar system capable of the early detection of incoming Exocet and Super Etendard missiles, and the facility to accurately report the missiles' positions, and estimated times of arrival, back to the task force ships.

Searchwater radar

Sea King helicopter with Searchwater radar

© *John Entwistle*

Derek Martin, a technical consultant to the Thorn EMI Radar Division, takes up the story:

> *"The MoD proposal was achieved by setting up a continuous meeting which started at 2.00pm on the Sunday afternoon and went on until 2.00am the following morning, with people going away, doing a particular required task, and reporting back to the same meeting. By the end of this meeting every aspect of production, cost, programme and support was known.*
>
> *The proposal and costings were finished at 10.00am, and, after one modification to the price, Tom Mayer signed them off at 11.30am.*
>
> *Just eleven weeks from receiving instructions to generate a feasibility study, the first two helicopters fitted with the new Searchwater system left to join HMS Illustrious on her way to the Falklands."*

It was a herculean task and the story would be told and retold with justifiable pride.

RESTRUCTURE

In 1985 Colin Southgate, who had been in charge of the company's Information Technology Division, took over as Thorn EMI's managing director. Southgate's plan was to concentrate on the basic industries upon which Thorn and EMI had been separately built, and he soon initiated a dramatic programme of rationalisation and disposal, taking the cash generated from sales and ploughing it back into the company's core areas.

ARC

Before the merger with EMI, Thorn was already heavily involved in the manufacture of ticket-issuing machines and associated products. Using EMI Electronics' (now Thorn EMI Electronics) expertise and facilities, the company began developing a new integrated ticketing system that was to transform travelling on public transport, and form a major part of the work at Wells for many years to come.

Today we take for granted the speed, ease, and flexibility with which we buy tickets for mass transportation systems. However, issuing, checking, validating, and collecting and reconciling ticket revenue is an extremely complex business. In the days before micro-processors the process was labour-intensive, expensive, and a source of constant frustration for the travelling public.

Thorn EMI's revolutionary Access and Revenue Control (ARC) System seamlessly integrated clerk-operated ticket-issuing, portable ticket-issuing (PORTIS), self-service ticket machines, platform ticket verifiers (PLATIS), and automatic ticket barriers.

Not only that, but Thorn EMI Electronics also offered a comprehensive design service for access and revenue control systems. A team of specialised engineers based at the Wells site was available to prepare detailed plans, covering both system software and hardware specifications to meet specific operator's needs, and then implement those plans.

Ticket machine

Thorn EMI Electroniccs management and staff photographed with barrier equipment

Passenger using prototype Travelog for buses

The team used sophisticated computer-based techniques and equipment, which enabled it to model the operation of a system in order to prove its capability and to optimise its performance.

Just one year after its launch, the company's portable ticket-issuing system was in regular service on British Rail, and received an enthusiastic reception from passengers and British Rail employees alike. British Rail's project manager Roger Temple said at the time, "*It has been a great success. We have had no problems*" – a fitting tribute to the hard work of the team at Wells.

In 1988 the Wells team released a significantly upgraded version of its highly successful portable ticket-issuing system PORTIS. It gave the upgraded system the imaginative acronym SPORTIS (Super Portable Ticket-Issuing System) and was soon celebrating an order from British Rail to supply over 2,000 of the new units over the following two years.

Less than a year later the ARC team at Wells won a contract to supply and install access and fare control equipment to the Istanbul Transportation Company for use on the city's new metro system.

In February, Brian Harris (operations manager), Wayne Clements and Julian Day (software engineers), and Roger Webb (design engineer) left peaceful Wells for the considerably more earthly delights of Istanbul, to help with the installation of the system.

Julian Day told of the three weeks spent in Istanbul:

> *"Most people think of Istanbul as a typically eastern city with mosques, minarets and golden sunsets. This is the Istanbul most tourists see on their package holidays. To get a real feel for the city you have, firstly, to work there and, secondly, to travel everywhere by taxi.*
>
> *As we discovered during our three week stay, this guarantees that you will get to see the other side of Istanbul. We were helped by taxi drivers who all appeared to know different routes to our headquarters and the newly built station. This led to mystery tours around areas of the city even the locals didn't know existed.*
>
> *The city spans the Golden Horn, once an important trading centre in days gone by. The majority of the city lies to the west of this and it's here that you discover the poorer regions of Istanbul.*
>
> *The houses appear to be only half built, the streets are covered either in dust or awash with a mud and cement slurry and the traffic is extremely congested. The new metro will provide alternative transport by rail and will help to ease the congestion.*
>
> *Every day brought us new problems and amusing moments. We were constantly surprised by the Turkish wiring standards, or should say, the lack of them. We were amazed that anything worked. Until you see someone push two wires into a wall socket and then run a drill off it you don't believe it is possible! We became very wary of bare wires that hung from every ceiling and that poked up through the floors.*
>
> *I think that our funniest moment came one day at the workshops. We had been waiting for a minibus to transport us and our equipment to one of the stations.*
>
> *We waited for about three hours before it finally arrived. Suddenly, people appeared from all directions, loaded our gear aboard, about six security guards jumped in, thereby filling the bus, closed the door and sped off.*

*They seemed to have totally forgotten us and we were left stranded in the middle
of the car park in total disbelief. Our time in Turkey was frequently punctuated by
moments like that. These helped to alleviate the feeling of frustration that followed
us from one hiccup to another.*

*The highlight of the job was actually seeing the metro carrying real passengers on
Saturday March 11th when the first stage was opened by Mr Bedrettin Datan,
the Mayor. This made all the hard work worthwhile.*

*Mr Datan declared free rides for the citizens of Istanbul for the first fifteen days
that the metro was opened. On the first Sunday, people using the train were so
excited that no-one was getting off which meant that by mid-morning people were
crammed into the carriages with their faces pressed hard against the windows
and doors.*

We decided to catch a taxi and live dangerously just one more time."

MISSION SUPPORT SYSTEMS

The second half of the1980s was a busy and productive period for the Wells site.
As well as designing and manufacturing innovative military products such as harsh
environment recorders (HERS), and an electronic support system (CORVUS)
that could detect the presence of enemy ships without revealing its own position;
it was refining and improving its groundbreaking mission support system (MSS)
technology.

Back in 1980 EMI Wells won the initial contract as lead supplier for a ground-based
Nimrod (Mk2) Mission Support System (MSS) primarily aimed at fulfilling the RAF
requirement for fast-time replay and reconstruction of the aircraft's underwater
acoustic detection capability. The system was to be an operational tool aimed at
informing aircrew of the 'live operational scenario', not a research/analysis system.

The contract was won in competition with much bigger companies such as GEC
and BAE. It was a landmark victory for the comparatively small subdivision at Wells,
which had previously only delivered sub-contracts supporting the 'head-office' sites
at Hayes and Feltham. Winning the MSS contract was the first opportunity for
Wells to act as prime supplier for a large contract for the MoD. It was a step-change
in the evolution of the Wells management style.

Early MSS thought to be at RAF St Mawgan

The contract having been awarded, the next step was to draw up the exact MSS contract specification and the contract value, things that were to evolve significantly over the next five years. The project was supported and managed by the Wells project team led by George Young with the active participation of the MoD Operational Requirement Establishment, the MoD(PE), and a team of eight Wells-based RAF Liaison Officers representing the RAF Nimrod Operating squadrons.

The first Mission Support Systems (MSS) delivered in 1986 were not the stand-alone acoustic replay systems that conformed to the original requirements specification. The MSS had by now grown into a truly comprehensive mission support system, which was fully networked and multi-station capable. It incorporated innovative commercial IT standards within a defence security wrapper. Using commercial standards and commercial hardware was a strategy that would serve the Penleigh team well as it strove to break through the taboo surrounding defence procurement against it using commercial technology. After the initial delivery in 1986 the MSS system benefited from a continual development contractual framework that has lasted until the present day.

MSS formed the backbone of the mission support product line that the Wells site went on to develop, and that eventually replaced much of the waning production and research work.

HUTTON MOOR, RADIO (RADAR) MODELLING

As we noted in Chapter Three, much of the research work at Wells relied on modelling radar signals of military vehicles of all types: land, sea and air. Once the radar signal specific to each vehicle type (for example a class of ship, a type of plane, or a kind of tank) had been accurately measured using scale models, the unique signature of that vehicle could be recognised in future. This meant that in live battlefield situations, a particular radar signal could be accurately identified as originating from a specific vehicle rather than just generic 'objects'.

Writing in the company newsletter '*Database*' in 1987, Pam Hillier provided a concise and entertaining history of the activities of the 'modelling groups'.

> *"In addition to its offices in Wells, the Radar Target Modelling Department, part of Consultancy Services, has people working twenty miles away, in an isolated aircraft hangar on the windswept airfield near Weston-super-Mare, carrying out radar signature measurements of scale models of land, sea and air vehicles.*
>
> *In the beginning it was hoped to be located a little nearer the Penleigh site. There was an opportunity to take over the old cinema at Cheddar, but investigations in 1958 proved it not to be large enough and it did not have a load-bearing roof.*
>
> *As it turned out, the Ministry of Supply (now MoD) decided to allow the use of one third of the then semi-derelict Flight Shed No.1 on Weston Airfield. Behind a purpose built, three metre high brick wall, the remaining two thirds of the building were used to house old aircraft used for RAF training.*
>
> *Improvements in working conditions were rather slow at first, but technology came thick and fast after the arrival of the first computer (an ICL 903c) in 1968. There are now (1987) thirteen mini computers on site at the hangar, with numerous peripherals, add-ons and plug-ins.*

Models at Hutton Moor

Members of Hutton Moor and Wells staff attending the retirement presentation for Geoff Wilson

From left to right: Robert Taylor, Doug Hancorn, Fred Townsend, Dudley Bird, John Latchford, Dave Chorley, Malcolm Evans, Alan Shields, Phil Chir, Mike Graham, Dave Crowcombe, Ray Ford, Gwen Bragg, John Turnock, Andy Bond, Peter Dickens, Jon Hutton, Tony Church, Fred Cook, James Bairstow, Terry Ellaway, Andy Ham, Graham Tupper, Greg Villis, Dave Gill, Andy Pritchard, Marion Wilson, Geoff Wilson, Pete Spencer, Jerry Gepps, Richard Bowery

Pam Hillier with a model Harrier at Hutton Moor

So who are these people hidden away in this remote corner of the countryside? Well, there's the deputy manager of the whole department, Dudley Bird, and then there are measurement teams, model shop craftsmen, radar technicians, computer hardware and software engineers, general office staff, cleaning and maintenance personnel, project planners and co-ordinators and our very own publications area, not forgetting all of the security police.

There are even people who remember the beginnings of the UK National Radar Target Modelling Measurement Facility. Les Wilkins will be with us for a good few years yet, but Jim Crowe, site manager of the hangar since 1958, retires this year (Sept 1987).

There are advantages and disadvantages to life at Weston. For instance, we have no drinks or vending machines on site – we have to be content to have our tea/ coffee made for us at 10.30am and 3.30pm. At these times, a klaxon sounds and then, what seems like a totally empty building suddenly comes alive as everyone emerges from their various holes in the woodwork to congregate in our 'canteen'. Actually we have no canteen facilities as such but an arrangement with the Arosfa Hotel in town which means a mass exodus every lunchtime.

The measurement facility continues to develop under the direction and funding of the MoD. We are now entering a phase of expansion in certain areas to

*accommodate the ever increasing demands of our customers. That we are able
to do so in the present economic climate is an indication of the confidence felt by
Ministry of Defence and others concerned in our future."*

The modelling groups made use of the quietness and seclusion of the original
Underwood Quarry close to the Penleigh site, to make measurements of vehicles
on turntables or suspended from a crane jib.

RADAR AUTOMATIC TRACK EXTRACTOR (RATE)

In the same year that Pam was writing, the company won a bid to supply Royal
Navy ships with radar automatic track extractor (RATE) equipment, developed and
manufactured in Wells.

RATE was a system designed to exploit the radar returns from ship-borne
navigation radar and associated equipment, and make this information available for
use by command, control and weapons systems. Initially the units were scheduled
for fitting in new surface vessels in the shipyards, but a retro-fitting programme for
existing ships was also under consideration.

Like the MSS project there was potential in RATE for repeat orders into the 1990s,
and the opportunity to sell similar equipment to other home and overseas buyers.

MICROWAVE COMMUNICATION

Back in 1968 Gordon Selby (the Wells radar guns expert witness, who also worked
on the Apollo Moon mission) was working in California when he invited Len
Cram, part of the Wells team, to a barbeque at his home. It must have been a good
party because Len subsequently asked Gordon to join him at Wells to start up a
communications laboratory.

Their pioneering research, done in collaboration with the Post Office, produced a
series of experimental digital radio links, including the world's first 11GHz point-to-
point link between Birmingham and Charwelton.

Unfortunately, there was no follow-on work from BT for the 11GHz microwave
digital link. The big companies in the field were put out by EMI's intrusion, and when
there was new work to tender for, GEC Marconi undercut EMI's bid. It wasn't until
about 1980 that another opportunity in communications arose.

In the 1980s, liberalisation of competition laws allowed Mercury Communications (part of the Cable & Wireless company) and others to open up the market for digital microwave links and satellite communications using this technology. Wells quickly responded to the challenge, setting up a Communications Division at Wells under Brian Jackson and Gordon Selby, and winning orders for digital microwave links from Mercury and the Wales Gas Board. Microwave links were provided for the first cellular mobile phones. Several hundred masts were interconnected with microwave links, in partnership with Nera; and so the whole of London was covered.

Also at about this time, a contract was won to develop and manufacture an advanced microprocessor-controlled point-to-multipoint system for BT's KiloStream TDMA data transmission service operating at 19GHz over a digital microwave link. John Ogborne was involved. 20 sets were produced.

In the Spring of 1988, Wells went on to win orders from British Telecom International (BTI) and the Independent Broadcasting Authority (IBA) to supply and install radio communications equipment for two large satellite earth stations. This was effectively the start of commercial satellite broadcasting, but, already alive to the possibility of negative publicity, a Wells media spokesperson was at pains to point out that:

> *"There's no need to worry about having the garden taken over by huge satellite dishes — a two-foot diameter dish suffices for Astra and a one-foot dish for BSB."*

Following the merger with Thorn, the managing director Tom Mayer, who was very keen on communications, gave his full support. The company started making satellite earth stations and links for British Telecom and Cable & Wireless. However, after several years and many successes, the parent company decided to pull out of microwave communications. Brian Jackson, the leader of the microwave team, was now appointed Chief Scientist (Wells), a position he held until his retirement in 1991.

FULL-SCALE RADAR MEASUREMENT

Over this period, the Wells team developed a series of full-scale fully-instrumented high-resolution radar measurement systems (MCR, MIMDAS, MIDAS, ADAS), under the leadership of John Mackenzie. These radars systems, developed in-house, were elegantly designed, and while increasing in capability and sophistication, were continually reducing in size. The earliest was housed in a large lorry trailer, while the

Chinook lowering a Harrier Jet into Underwood Quarry

ADAS system, probably the most refined, was capable of being fitted in a helicopter, together with radar operator.

Complementing the scale-modelling work at Weston-super-Mare, radar systems were transported to sites throughout the UK and abroad to carry out trials, measure full-size military assets, and characteristics of ocean surfaces and various types of terrain.

The 'full-scale' team had a good reputation for getting on with the job, and producing excellent results quickly, often in challenging and testing locations including the peaks of some significant mountains.

In order to be able to carry out measurements closer to home, the Underwood Quarry was used together with a turntable and crane. Infra-red facilities were installed in the quarry alongside the radar facilities.

RESTRUCTURE

In the early 1990s Southgate further focused the company's interests until there were effectively only two – the rental business and music. The software business was disposed of in 1991, and two years later Thorn EMI sold its lighting division, the business upon which the Thorn side had been founded.

In 1994, as the group poured money into its music operations, Thorn Security was jettisoned, and by 1995 the company had sold its defence businesses, including its electronics division. Once again the operation at Wells found itself at the mercy of the cut-throat world of international conglomerates.

Ironically, business at the Penleigh site was flourishing.

SALE

On 31 March 1995 Racal Radar Defence Systems, a subsidiary of Racal Electronics purchased what was by then known as the Sensors Group of Thorn EMI Electronics. The Sensors Group comprised the operations in Wells and Crawley, which now became known as Racal-Thorn Defence.

Racal Electronics plc was a multinational manufacturer and service provider in telecommunications, security, data communications, defence radar and avionics, marine and energy electronics, radio communications, and specialised electronics.

A conglomerate of some 150 medium-sized, autonomous companies, Racal operated through a network of subsidiaries in England, the United States, Europe and Asia. Twenty of these subsidiaries were in North America. Overall, sales outside of the United Kingdom accounted for more than 54% of Racal's annual revenues.

Racal-Thorn Defence itself comprised Racal Radar Defence and the Thorn Sensors Group acquired by Racal in 1995. It was a member of the Racal Electronics Group with over 100 operating companies world-wide accounting for 30% of the group's turnover of more than £1 billion. Racal Thorn's principal activities were now in the fields of electronic warfare, command information systems, advanced radar systems, and radio communications.

NEW JOBS AT WELLS FACILITY

When Racal-Thorn Defence took over the EMI Sensors Group 450 staff were employed at Wells. The transition from Thorn EMI had gone smoothly and the company was thriving. The workforce had developed key strengths in high-technology manufacturing processes, software design and programme management. They were already involved in some of the MoD's most sophisticated equipment procurement programmes including the replacement Maritime Patrol Aircraft, the Royal Navy's Merlin helicopter, and the Army's Apache attack helicopter.

The company soon announced it was to create 50 new high-technology jobs in Wells over the following year. The vacancies were mainly in hardware and software engineering, and were a result of an order book that totalled in excess of £60 million.

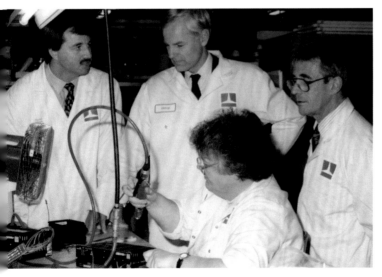

Richard Moon, then managing director of Racal-Thorn Defence in Wells, commented at the time:

"Racal's defence electronics business has continued to thrive despite the world decline in defence budgets. We are a

Richard Moon,
David Heathcoat-Amory MP,
Barry Jones and Ruth Curtain

progressive company and have established ourselves as a centre of excellence in some specific areas of advanced defence electronics technology. We are seeking to recruit 50 new staff that will have the drive and commitment to take part in a West Country success story."

Work positions in UK TACC operator shelter

In August 1997, Racal was awarded a contract from the UK MoD for the UK Tactical Air Control Centre (UK TACC). The system was to provide a mobile, modular Air Command and Control (AC2) system designed to provide tactical support to Rapid-Reaction Forces engaged in expeditionary operations and to conduct the management of an air defence battle.

The system is packaged into ten 6.1metre (20-foot) ISO shelters equipped with the voice and data communications necessary to interface with: other sensors and intelligence platforms; maritime and land tactical control formations; weapons platforms; higher command formations; and different types of active and passive sensors, thus providing the ability to build a Recognised Air Picture.

The UK TACC entered service with the Royal Air Force No.1 Air Control Centre in December 2002 and has since been actively supporting extended UK deployed operations. Between May 2003 and January 2004 it was deployed in support of Op TELIC, and more recently has completed a thirty-nine month deployment in support of Op. HERRICK and NATO's International Security Assistance Force. During this operation the UK TACC was described as 'Essential to Operations', and as one of the world's few deployable ground-based air-surveillance units, can now genuinely be regarded as Operationally Proven.

A CHANGE OF EMPHASIS

Over the previous 20 years the balance between manufacturing and R&D at Wells had gradually shifted.

In the early Scophony years various facilities had been established in Wells to support the R&D activities of the company. The Penleigh site soon had a comprehensive manufacturing operation that gave the scientists and engineers complete process capability, from receipt of raw material through machining, plating and painting, assembly and final testing. Manufacturing played a major role in the profitability of the Wells site throughout the 60s, 70s, and 80s.

Assembly and wiring areas manufactured various complex products including telemetry for missiles such as the Sea Wolf, Sea Dart, Sea Skua and Bloodhound, as well as sonar buoys, inspection cameras for early Concorde passenger jets, and

Drawing Office in Building Two

Working on the Wiring Line

marine radar systems. During the late 70s and early 80s two 'clean rooms' were set up to allow assembly to be carried out in a precisely-controlled environment. At the time these facilities were amongst the most advanced of their type in the UK.

The mid 80s saw a downturn in MoD orders that involved manufacture, and so the emphasis moved from military to predominantly civil work. The highly successful British Rail contract for ticketing systems and related hardware (ARC, ACTIS, PORTIS and APTIS outlined earlier in this chapter) was fulfilled from the Wells site.

A machine shop had been established in the 1960s to support the need for the manufacture of high-precision components. The machine shop was manned by a team of highly-skilled craftsmen, many of them having graduated from an EMI apprentice scheme that typically involved up to five years of intensive training.

In the late 70s, Computer Numerically Controlled (CNC) machines arrived that were capable of turning out consistently reputable results from a single initial computer programme. This development subsequently led to the decline and eventual closure of the machine shop; its work now being completely outsourced.

Alongside the assembly and wiring areas and the machine shop, a model shop was set up to manufacture the highly-detailed and accurate scale models that the Hutton Moor team needed for their scaled radar signature measurements.

Whereas at its height, manufacturing work at the Wells site represented at least 50% of the turnover of the company, by the 1990s that figure had reduced to less than 10%, with a consequent shift in the make-up of the workforce.

The company had to adapt to changing circumstances, and was now out-sourcing the vast majority of manufacturing to other specialist companies. However, throughout the 1990s a series of large defence development contracts ensured the continued success of the Penleigh site.

These multi-million pound projects included the Ground Entry Terminal System (GETS); the Air Platform Network Management System; the UK Tactical Joint Information Distribution System Facility (JTIDS); a mission debrief system for the Eurofighter; and radar decoy systems for Lockheed Martin.

Racal-Thorn, a truly global company, had already sold the Chinese a number of Cymbeline artillery-locating radars during the 1980s. Now after three years of hard negotiations it concluded a £40 million deal to sell them eight surveillance radar systems.

These systems were variants of Searchwater, the system that Thorn EMI had developed, and that had been in service with Royal Air Force Nimrod squadrons since the 1970s. It was eventually superseded by the Searchwater 2000 radar, which was fitted in the British Aerospace Nimrod 2000.

Cymbeline radar

THOMSON-CSF

At the turn of the 21ˢᵗ century everything appeared to be flourishing at the Penleigh site, but once again events on the international stage played their part in the company's destiny.

The UK government, by far Racal Defence's biggest customer, wanted to consolidate the defence sector to encourage more competition at 'prime supplier' level, while at the same time protecting the industry from growing competition around the world.

As a consequence, in June 2000, Thomson-CSF, a French company, made a friendly takeover bid of £1.3 billion for Racal Electronics. The bid was accepted, and the merger of these two medium-sized companies, now renamed Thomson-CSF Racal plc, made the newly-formed company the second largest company in the UK defence industry after BAE.

MORE PHOTOS . . .

*Early 1980s
Apprentices*

*From left to right:
Dino Gallo,
Matthew Ramsay,
Mark Towlson,
Gary Lockyer,
Simon Ring,
Sharon Morgan,
Paul Clayton,
Troy Chivers,
Robert Davis,
Lester Coles,
Miles Warren*

*Apprentices with Dick Newton
(Apprentice Training Manager
(centre back)*

*Apprentices including
Mike Prout, Mark Grant,
Pete Dickens, Andy Bond and
Steve Ferris*

Apprentices 1985 - Display of work completed in the Training Centre

From left to right: Bruce Harris, Colin Grist, James Bowring, Dick Newton (Apprentice Training Manager), Pete Hoddinott, Scott Cunliffe, Rachel Knight (née Searle), Mike Court, Rob Hathway, Darren Wilson, Stuart Davis, Andrew Holford, John Reynolds, Andy Carpenter

Long Service Awards, 25 years, presented by Richard Moon, (MD) to Dave Pullen, Dudley Bird, Steve Craft, Tom Billing, John Grimshaw and Andy Burtle

Apprentices 1988-89

From left to right:
Steve De Bruin, Ed Parfitt,
Ryan Wallls, Nick Thorne,
Andrew Mitchell,
Darren Shepherd, Lee James

Apprentices 1989-90

From left to right:
Andrew Hitchings,
Shane Rice, Rob Grout,
Gareth Padgett, Steve Hole,
Andrew Rhymer,
Steve Cooper,
Phillips Griffiths

Apprentices 1990-91

Back row from left right:
Craig Symms,
Darrell Gill, Andrew Stock,
Mark Isgrove,
Russell Carlton,
Adrian Jones

Front row from left to right:
Simon Cavill, Stuart Bush,
Spencer Manly,
Jeremy Middleton,
Emma (surname unknown)

Careers at Wells winners

From left to right:
Andrew Hitchings, Gareth Padgett,
Paul Moore and Rodney Foster

EMI Datatech Team at the Mill c.1985

Above: From Left to right: David Moore, Darren Wilson, Alan Donson (Principal of Strode College, Street), Mike Penery (MD Thorn EMI Electronics), Mark Parsons, Robert Moon

Apprentice Awards presented by Mike Penery

On the occasion of Dick Newton's retirement in 1987 including all the apprentices working with him, at that time, within the Thorn EMI apprenticeship scheme

Front Row left to right: Lee Neale, Mark Russell, Rodney Foster, Matthew Say, John Coombes, Jon Phelps, Craig Smith, Mark Bennetts, Darren Appleby

Second Row left to right: Andrew Halford, Colin Grist, Mike Court, Scott Cunliffe, Angela McDonald (née Davidson), Dick Newton (Apprentice Training Manager), Rachel Knight (née Searle), Darren Wilson, Pete Hoddinott, Bruce Harris, Stuart Davis

Back row left to right: Gary Andrews, James Bowring, Andrew Cornish, Keith Hamblin, Alan Newton, Peter Ullyatt, Ed Brown-Kenyon, Martyn Hill, Andrew Baker, Michael Bragg, Chris Hancock, Andrew Bird, Paul Lancaster, Andrew Reeson, Martin Greed, Mark Chipperfield, Mark McDonald, Richard Crowcombe, Andrew Chilvers, Michael Cook, Nigel Ferris, Mark Parsons, Robert Moon, David Rice, Barry Pritchard, Nick Tinknell

40 Year Long Service Awards November 1990

From left to right: Colin Church, John Prout, Colin Harrington, Bill White, Ray Brown, Maurice Elms

40 Year Long Service Award presented to Colin Harrington by Bill White in November 1990

25 and 40 Year Long Service Awards 1994

25 Years: Tim Wallis, Terry Ellaway, Terry Chivers, Malcolm Evans (far right)

40 Years: Ted Allen, Ken Vowles, Ted James

CHAPTER FIVE

The final chapter

The Penleigh site was not destined to be referred to as Thomson-CSF for long. On December 6th 2000 the company that bought Racal changed its name to Thales, and Thomson-CSF ceased to exist.

Partially owned by the French state, the Thales group is a major international force in the defence, security, aerospace and mass transport markets. The group is the 11th largest defence contractor in the world; in 2010 it generated revenues of £11.2 billion, operated in 50 countries and employed 68,000 individuals.

In Britain, Thales UK employs approximately 8,500 people in more than 40 locations. As well as defence, Thales has a large civil operation with particular expertise in secure network communications, and technologies involved in mass transportation systems.

As usual life at the Wells site quickly adapted to the new owner's specific interests. The majority of the 'live' projects begun under previous ownerships were simply absorbed into Thales, while work on new Thales projects began to filter through, taking advantage of the unique resource the company had acquired in Wells.

It is a tribute to the team at Wells that business flourished at Penleigh in spite of the numerous changes of ownership, mergers, de-mergers, and restructuring exercises that beset them since the birth of the Penleigh site.

Indeed many of the most notable achievements of the Thales UK Wells era were related to projects that had their origins at Wells decades previously, and that the Wells team had continued to deliver successfully, in spite of turmoil at a succession of 'head offices'.

Notable 21st century successes at the Penleigh site include the following.

EUROFIGHTER

The Wells site first became involved in the Eurofighter project in 1998, when Racal's exploratory discussions with Espelsa (Spain), Dornier (Germany) and Alenia Difesa (Italy) resulted in the formation of a multi-national consortium to bid for the Mission Planning and Briefing (MPB) system for the Typhoon aircraft. This was the first multinational consortium with which the engineers and scientists at Wells had been involved with, and introduced a new collaborative way of developing products and technologies that was to become the norm in the 21st century.

While Espelsa led the MPB programme, it provided a platform from which Racal was able to successfully lead the consortium for bidding for the Mission Debriefer (MDB) system. Thales UK took over the bid, and won the MDB contract in 2000.

Involvement in the Eurofighter programme led to Thales developing a UK-specific solution – the Typhoon Mission Data Exchange (TMDX) system for the RAF in 2008.

Eurofighter   © *John Entwistle*

In 2010 the TMDX team at Wells was awarded a Chief of Defence Material (CDM) Commendation for its contribution to the system that saw its first combat mission in 2011, supporting the Libyan no-fly zone.

Eurofighter TMDX team with their CDM commendation

From left to right: Stuart Parr, Rob Passmore, Susan Dale, Derek Gatt, Sharon Harms, Mike Hicks, Richard Bessant, Mark Rixton, Barry Miller, Craig Smith, Graham Adkins, Val Knowles, Jim Morrison, Rob Probert, Chris Ashworth, Chris Gollop, Jon Snell, Eliott Hall, James Senior, Chris Williams, Darren Shepherd, Matt Taylor, Paul Luxton, Ashley Parkes, Nick Collins, Rob Clanchy, David Lockwood, Vince Smith (MD Air Operations)

A CDM commendation recognises an achievement of outstanding merit beyond performance expectations that is worthy of senior management and public recognition. The award ceremony took place at the main MoD building in Whitehall, London. Jon Snell, MSS Engineering Manager, and a key member of the joint team, represented Thales UK Wells.

Thales UK Wells was a central player in the team that defined the business case, architecture, and components of the new UK Typhoon MSS. Once this was defined the Wells team contributed major elements to the new system, which aided the aircrew to improve its overall debriefing process and effectively manage all of the Typhoon's multi-mission data.

DARS

In 2003 Thales won the contract for the DARS (deployable, air control centre, recognised air picture production centre, sensor fusion post) element of the NATO Air Command and Control System (ACCS) programme that provides an overall command and control system for the whole of the NATO operational area.

The DARS system is designed to be speedily deployable and capable of supporting NATO operations in any theatre of operation. It is packaged into 20-foot units based on highly modified sea containers, the number of units deployed being scalable to support the required size of deployment.

Operator positions in DARS shelter

Following testing and trials for mobility, reliability, and operational performance, Thales delivered the first fully operational systems at the end of 2006.

NATO subsequently commissioned a 'quick reaction' version of DARS to provide an even more rapidly deployable configuration to support rapid reaction forces. The DARS units are currently garrisoned at Nieuw Milligen in the Netherlands, and manned by a multinational contingent of operators and technicians.

SIGNATURE MANAGEMENT

By the mid 2000s, the modelling groups at Wells had become known as the Signature Management department. The team's unique ability to formulate the radar signatures of specific objects from detailed scale models had led to new systems that reduced the probability of detection by enemy sensors. It did this by reducing the 'contrast' between the platform and the environment that it is operating in – in simple terms, electronic camouflage.

In modern warfare, the vital element of stealth that an armed force can achieve depends on its

A model and radar cross-section of a Chieftain tank

management of the various signatures (sound, light, heat, and radar reflections) that it generates. By 2006, the Wells Signature Management Department's work was so highly valued by the MoD that they awarded it a three-year contract to 'secure the availability of physical assets to UK MoD customers including radar measurement, equipment.'.

The contract is a tangible recognition of the dedication of the various modelling groups at Wells (and the Hutton Moor outpost) that can be traced unbroken back to the first years of the Penleigh site.

FALCON

In the same year, 2006, Thales UK Wells won a major contract from BAE Systems, worth in excess of £50 million, to supply the transmission and security sub-systems for the British Army's FALCON programme.

The FALCON system provides powerful digital communications networks for controlling combat operations at corps, divisional and brigade level. It has up to fifty times the capability of the systems it replaced, and has resulted in a massive improvement in the Army's communications network, leading to a significant reduction in the number of vehicles and personnel needed to support a major tactical headquarters.

Talking at the time, Alex Dorrian, Chief Executive of Thales UK said:

> *"Thales UK has for many years been at the forefront of military communications. We have secured a key role on this critical information infrastructure project and have made a major contribution to the BAE Systems team. The programme will ensure that our capabilities in this area will continue to develop for the future."*

ISTAR MSS

In 1985 the MSS team at Wells delivered the first 'Intelligence Surveillance Target Acquisition and Reconnaissance' (ISTAR) Mission Support System (MSS) to the RAF. The project continued to develop throughout all the changes of ownership at Wells, and in 2006, Air Systems in Wells celebrated winning a further five-year multi-million pound deal to support the project.

Some of the MSS team had been with the project since its birth 20 years earlier, and had become known as 'Lifers'. It was only fitting that the work of these Lifers should be recognised at a special dinner to celebrate the ongoing success of the project.

Presentation at RAF Kinloss

Ground left: Mike Hooper, Geoff Cawthorne, Angharad Jones, Warren Smythe, Graham Miller, Flt. Lt. Rachel Cochran, Pete Hayes, Peter Abbotts, Rachel Knight, Gary Sims

Foreground: Capt George Baher, Wing Commdr T. Dennington, Steve Hill

Ground right: Scott McVicar, Barry Ashby, Ian Hooper, Barry Greenhalgh, Kevin Pond, Ashley Parkes

Stairs left: Roger Tarttelin, Mike Cohen (CSF), Derek McNeir (QQ), Tony Scragg, Ed Silvester

Stairs right: Trevor Harris, Stewart Wright, Sandy McGregor, Ken Bishop, Kevin Butcher

The Lifers group took part in a gala dinner at Kinloss in Scotland on 12th October 2005, attended by Steve Hill, Managing Director of Air Systems at Wells, Ashley Parkes, Business Director for Airbase Operations together with members of the Thales UK project team from both Wells and Kinloss.

RAF personnel, senior members of the MSS operating community, and representatives from industry also attended what must have been an unforgettable evening. The dinner was followed the next day by a formal contract award ceremony at the operations centre of the RAF Kinloss base.

'Lifer' Geoff Cawthorne, then software project engineer, and later promoted to MSS Business Manager said at the time:

> *"I think the success of the project has been due to the good working relationship developed over many years with the customer and the user community. They love coming to visit us in Wells and we have been able to meet all of their expectations at all levels."*

His fellow Lifer Ken Bishop added,

> *"MSS is a unique community with a blend of friendliness and professionalism marked out by its wonderful array of characters."*

FUTURE INTEGRATED SOLDIER TECHNOLOGY

Early in 2007 Thales UK Wells signed a contract that extended another of its ongoing programmes, Future Integrated Soldier Technology (FIST). The new contract focussed on 'the assessment of surveillance and target acquisition and command, control, computer, communications and information (C4I) systems'.

C4I systems can include radios, computing, navigation, displays, and command and control software that provide situational awareness at platoon-level and below, with easily understood, continually updated information.

The equipment involved in the new FIST programme included sights for infantry section weapons, range finding, and target acquisition equipment for day and night use. The new hardware and software substantially enhanced the infantry's ability to detect, recognise and identify targets, and 'engage them effectively' once acquired.

WATCHKEEPER AND CIVIL UAVS

On April 14 2010 the Watchkeeper unmanned air system (UAS) made its maiden UK flight, taking off from dedicated facilities at Parc Aberporth in West Wales for a 20-minute flight.

The success of the flight was the first milestone in a long-term programme by an integrated Thales UK team, which included Wells and the MoD team, to demonstrate that the Watchkeeper system meets the robust safety and airworthiness criteria required to fly unmanned airborne vehicles (UAVs) initially on ranges and in segregated airspace in the UK.

Unmanned air system

The Watchkeeper system enables commanders on the ground to detect and track targets for many hours without having to deploy troops in to sensitive or dangerous areas. The system is capable of rapid deployment for operations anywhere in the world and supports the information requirements of all three services.

Commenting on the maiden flight, Alex Dorrian, CEO of Thales UK, said,

> *"This is a momentous accomplishment in the Watchkeeper programme, and is just one of a number of flight trials scheduled over the coming months. This milestone reflects the years of hard work by Thales UK, the MoD and other parties since the contract was signed."*

Watchkeeper was an exclusively military programme, but there was increasing interest in the use of UAVs for civil purposes, including providing commanders with a safe overview of incidents such as major fires, industrial accidents, or ecological disasters, and supporting complex search-and-rescue missions.

Thales UK Wells took an active part in ASTRAEA, a collaborative programme involving the UK government, industry and academia to examine civil use of UAV technology.

GRADUATE TRAINING

In 2006 Wells became a full member of the Thales graduate scheme, a UK-wide initiative to recruit, train, and develop outstanding graduates in the first stages of their transition from academic to professional life.

After initial selection, graduates were appointed to one of the Thales' locations across the UK, and regularly met with colleagues from Thales' international operations during the four years of their course.

At one time as many as 30 members of the graduate scheme worked at Thales at Wells, where an established community at the site and a welcoming city made it a popular posting.

Talking about the scheme, Ricky Clayton, currently a systems engineer with the ISTAR MSS project said:

> *"As an introduction to engineering, it has been absolutely priceless. I'll take*

Graduates 2008

From left to right:
Matthew Rich,
Sam Crowther,
David Lee Jones

Graduates 2008

John Wallace,
Kate Mallichan,
Sam Eggleton,
Duncan Curtis,
Richard Ferrario,
Ricky Clayton, Tim Skinner

Graduates 2009

Chris Pennack,
Matt Robinson, Nigel
Maycock,
Luke McDowell,
Stuart Greenhall,
James Bewley

everything I've learned on it to my next project, and this will stand me in good stead as I begin to tackle the next big hurdle – project management."

Graduates are encouraged to support educational schemes with the local schools, mentoring groups through their GCSE projects, and giving students the opportunity to find out what life in university and beyond was like.

Wells graduates have frequently worked with the local Blue School, raising the awareness of science, technology and engineering as exciting subjects with the potential to open up all kinds of career opportunities. As well as supporting projects such as National Science and Engineering Week, graduates visited local schools to talk about their work, demonstrate some of the technologies they were currently working on, and in some cases help students with GCSE and A-level projects.

Thales stand prepared by graduates at the annual Imagineering Fair held at the Royal Bath and West Show, Shepton Mallet

Spreading their net a little wider, graduates from Wells, Templecombe and other Thales sites, regularly participated in the annual Imagineering Fair held at the Royal Bath and West Show. The fair, staffed by volunteers, was a special initiative to introduce young people to the world of engineering through hands-on experience, and fun activities.

Victor Chavez, Deputy Chief Executive Thales UK, commented:

> *"Thales UK employs 8,500 throughout all regions of the UK, with a high proportion of staff being involved in science, technology and engineering. The themes of technology and education are at the heart of what we do, which is why we are so enthusiastic about supporting Imagineering.*
>
> *This is the sixth time that Thales UK has supported this event and we believe very strongly that this type of activity is crucial in raising the profile of engineering in the minds of young people as an exciting career for their future."*

Long Service Awards with Vince Smith, Managing Director

From left to right: Colin Grist (25), John Reynolds (25), Dave Pullen (40), Stuart Davis (25), Shirley Reeder (25) Vince Smith (MD), Rachel Knight (25), Darren Wilson (25), Rob Hathway (25)

WELLS SITE FINALLY CLOSES

On 26th May 2010 Thales UK announced that its Penleigh site would close in 2011. A 90-day consultation period began, and the 500 workers currently working at the site were all offered alternative employment at Thales' main Somerset site, Templecombe, or at the Basingstoke and Bristol sites.

The 'air operations' element of the business would relocate to Templecombe, while the national security and resilience business would move to Basingstoke and Bristol supported by hubs at Templecombe.

A company spokeswoman commented:

> *"We understand that this is a challenging time, but our employees are our most important asset and they are key to our success.*
>
> *It is crucial that we retain the considerable skills and experience of our people when moving forward.*
>
> *We are committed to supporting and consulting with our employees through these proposed changes."*

Although the announcement was sad news for the Wells team, it hardly came as a surprise. The closure was nothing to do with the failure of the workforce to deliver, or the quality and profitability of their work, but everything to do with the nature of the site itself.

It is a very real tribute to the many achievements of generations of its workers that the Penleigh site, developed from a temporary prisoner-of-war camp built in the mid 20th century, and so clearly unsuitable for the needs of a 21st century multi-national operation, should have survived as long as it did.

CHAPTER 6

'…occasional interruptions for impromptu turns and social interludes'

There can be little doubt that the city of Wells and the new arrivals from North London soon formed a bond that was to endure through all the various incarnations of the Penleigh site.

This was not so remarkable when you consider that the majority of workers at the site would inevitably have been neighbours in the city. At one point the workforce at Penleigh numbered 1,200 in a city that barely housed 10,000.

It's also fair to say that companies in the 1950s and 60s adopted a generally more paternal attitude to their employees than their 21st century multinational counterparts. Not only did they introduce apprentice schemes at work, but they also provided facilities where their employees could relax, socialise with their colleagues, and form special-interest groups.

Thus in 1951, almost as soon as it had acquired Scophony, EMI began an apprentice scheme at the Penleigh site, and bought some land in Chamberlain Street for a sports and social club for its new employees. The original club-house fell victim to a chip-pan fire in the late 1950s and was subsequently rebuilt, the new building forming part of the club that still exists today.

As well as the various societies, groups, pantomime visits, social events, and of course the thriving bar, there were numerous trips, visits, and outdoor events including the extremely popular annual Field Day.

The driving force behind events at the club, including many charitable events was often the apprentices committee which organised regular fundraising events, supported a range of local and national charities and a hosted a variety of lectures at the club.

The pictures and excerpts from event programmes that follow give a flavour of just how important the social side of life was both for the workers at the Penleigh site, and the city of Wells itself.

SNIPPETS FROM CHIP
(CEDAR HOUSE INFORMATION PUBLICATION)

Gardening Section - 1973 September Edition

Bulbs are now on sale at the hut. Hut closes on Saturday 20th for the winter months.

Mrs E Baird (Sec)

Sections Show - 1973

Wonderful day - sunshine, good supporting crowd to see an excellent display of flowers and decoration in various arrangements, vegetables including the longest runner bean and largest pumpkin which didn't quite push us out of the marquee! The children's section including photographs, Domestic and handicrafts were all very well supported.

The judges who attended the show remarked on the high standard of the exhibits, which gives great encouragement of all the exhibitors who worked very hard to stage their excellent efforts of all the classes ONE to SEVENTY TWO inclusive.

The Flower Section, namely the Chrysanths were outstanding indeed, the whole show blossomed out very well!

The Ladies' Section did a great job of refreshing the hot and thirsty crowd.   The helpers were :

Mrs Betty Hutchinson, Mrs Sue Bradfield and Mrs Chris Davidson; our thanks to them.

The sailing dinghies (*EMI had its own sailing club with boats and boathouse on the River Axe at Uphill*) added colour to the outside exhibits.

The Radio Section operated by George Martin was working hard in the far corner of the field.

The outdoor skittles was run very well for three days by Steve Dredge and Sue Bradfield. Winners were Martin Rumary and Mrs Coombes. This was at EMI works, adjacent to the canteen. The skittle alley was then moved by the Maintenance Department to the Sports and Social field for the show day. On the day it was run by Len Rumley who had a bit of bother with the wobbly pins, but got by OK and I gather added to the afternoon's entertainment. Winners were Fred Townsend and Mrs J Delaney.

Sports Report – December 1971

The note in last months Cedar Post stating we were gong to obtain a sports reporter certainly shook up all the EMI teams in their various fields of battle, as not one loss has been reported to the Sports Office.

Pride of Place must go to the newly formed EMI Snooker Team under the able leadership of Dudley Bird (S.R.D.) after losing their first match of the season (nerves we suspect) they are now showing their true colours and winning or drawing every match, well done chaps. By the way I am told that Alec Dalwood has not yet lost a league match, (he must be fooling on Saturday nights) as your reporter watched him one Saturday and his unorthodox play was fascinating to watch, if slightly bewildering and frustrating for his opponent, or partner, I couldn't tell which.

The football team had a poor start to the season, but happy to report they are at least climbing the table, with 5 points out of the last 6. The two wins being 6-1 & 7-0, trust those 13 goals didn't prove unlucky. I was told they keep loosing the ball at Wookey in the long grass, never mind lads keep it on island.

The Ladies skittles team have at last reached the top of their league, only losing one match out of 6 played, have to sign some of them for EMI "A" team. In the Men's leagues, the "A" team started well but seem to be running out of stamina in Div 1.

The Charles Kinlock Show – December 1973

The wine tasting evening held at Cedar house on 19th November was an unqualified success. It attracted an even larger crowd than last year, being a literal sell-out.

The star attraction of the evening was most certainly the malt whiskey/Scots wine blend called Scotsmac. This latest and well priced drink from Kinlocks can be purchased through the club and anyone wishing to do so should contact Fred Townsend.

Stop Press Specials

Here we are at last with Christmas almost upon us, and a fairly full programme for the month, the only disappointment this year being that we have lost the Machine Shop Christmas Party owing to lack of numbers now in the Machine shop.

Bingo will be on 4th, 11th and 18th (November) this month and owing to the popularity of the Christmas Bingo there will be two Christmas Bingo Sessions, these will be on 11th and 18th December.

The film show will be held on Friday 3rd December entitled Carry on Camping starring guess who?

The Wiring Section's party will be held on Friday 10th followed the following Friday 17th by The Ladies Section party.

The apprentice Party being on the 23rd.

Christmas Party

From left to right: Dave Izzard, Andy Alford, Martin (Taffy) Thomas, Keith Hamblin, Jim Bowring, Steve Harrington, Paul Clayton, Steve Ferris and in the foreground, Colin and Sue Bryant

The original
Cedar House
Club c.1952

The bar inside the first
Cedar House Club in the
early 1950s

The Sports and
Social Club
in the snow
storms of 1963.
The Wells
Secondary
Modern School
can be seen in
the background

Treasure Hunt at the Social Club c.1957-8

Field Day

Field Day

1955 Sports and Social Club – The First!

Sports Day 1961

Field Day 1961

Field Day 1962 held in the grounds of the EMI Sports Centre, Wells. A play at putting a man on the moon

*1962
Apprentice Run
from Hayes to
Wells*

*EMI Apprentice Association
Inter-Divisional Football
Trophy - still competed for
today*

*The new EMI
Sports and
Social Club bar
in the 1970s*

1970s Apprentice football team

Back Row: John Alford, Steve Carpenter, Mike Roberts, Graham Lukins, Ross Baker, Martin Rivers,
Larry Gaulton

Front Row: Kevin Fisher, Alan Bennett, Alan Roper, Colin Palmer, Tony Fricker

Miss EMI 1960

Miss EMI 1972

Miss EMI 1978

1959 Apprentices christmas party

EMI showband The Bootleggers

EMI Sports and Social Club awards

Sports Day 1982

Cup presentation during the 1980s

CHAPTER 7

And Finally ...

Some photographs of events that we have supported over the last few years.

Thales team competing at the Wells fun run

Back Row from left to right: Paula Casserly, Donna Newton, Alistair Smith, Roz Mundy, Bernie Mundy, Lee-Anne Cave, Rob Pay

Front Row from let to right: Rob Moore, Mary Harrington, Nina Conrad, David Alston-Pottinger

Ben Bonnick during his sponsored cycle ride to Paris, raising money for Help the Heroes

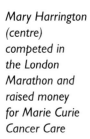

Mary Harrington (centre) competed in the London Marathon and raised money for Marie Curie Cancer Care

Thales 'We Miss
Ronaldo Too' football
team

Back row left to
right: Iain Shipman,
Mo Valuto,
Rob Evans,
Stuart Parr,
Christopher Ponton

Front row left to
right: Steve Jukes,
Hamish Hodder,
Jon Snell

In aid of Children's
Hospice South West

Thales 'Under
80s' football
team

From left to right:
Duncan Curtis,
Paul Copeland,
Stuart Morris,
Mayer Patel,
Darren Shepherd,
Darren Wilson,
Wayne Godsafe,
Geoff Bell

*Sophie Blinman practising for
her Great Wall of China trek in
aid of Marie Curie Cancer Care*

*Vince Smith performing a guitar
recital in aid of Marie Curie
Cancer Care*

Annual Pumpkin Competition

*From left to right:
Darren Wilson,
Emma Russell,
Sophie Blinman,
Debbie Owen,
Keith Taylor,
Lucy Burton,
Val Knowles,
Rob Moore,
Ann Taylor,
Phil Maxwell,
Harry Grainger*

Canteen staff, Sarah and Dave, putting their fruit and vegetables to good use in the snow

Ladies Driving Challenge
in aid of Marie Curie
Cancer Care

Standing: Ruth Vale,
Emma Russell,
Nicky Ganley, Liz Bowen,
Angie Thyer,
Sharon Marsh,
Susan Watkins,
Barbara Garner,
Sam Holmes,
Sophie Blinman,
Angela Waterhouse,
Debbie Owen

Front row: Andrea Adams,
Angharad Jones,
Sally Watkins

Children's Christmas
party, Wookey Hole

CHAPTER 8

In November 2011 Thales UK Wells ceased to exist

There were no more companies, multi-national or otherwise, waiting in the wings, so the final curtain came down on what was by any measure a remarkable story.

Members of the workforce who chose to stay with the company were offered jobs at Thales sites in Templecombe, Basingstoke and Bristol. For the first time in some 70 years the Penleigh site was silent.

Scophony's engineers and scientists arriving in Wells seeking temporary respite from the wartime bombing of London, could hardly have predicted the profound effect that the site at Penleigh was to have on the development of military and civil electronics, and on the life of their newly adopted home.

From the beginning the city of Wells responded enthusiastically to the new challenges. Not only did the city find places to live for these exotic newcomers, and places for the company could continue with its vital war work, it provided a local workforce that quickly learned the new skills that the company needed.

Of course the people of Wells were already hosting German and Italian prisoners of war with the same generosity of spirit that it extended to Scophony. During the war years Wells turned from a quiet market town to a cosmopolitan environment where locals, eastern European scientists, and prisoners of war could rub shoulders.

It is a tribute to the special qualities of the people of Wells that so many of the prisoners of war thanked them for their hospitality when the war finally ended. Indeed many later returned to Wells with their families to visit, and more than a few made the Somerset Levels their permanent home.

The ability of the city, and the workforce at the Penleigh site, to adapt to changing circumstances was to stand them in good stead as ownership of the site moved from company to company after Scophony merged with John Logie Baird Ltd, and then succumbed to EMI.

In many ways the chequered history of the site's ownership reflected what was going on generally in the development and production of complex electronic technology.

Small companies like Scophony, which had concentrated on one or two corners of the market, were gradually absorbed into larger conglomerates, until the UK electronics industry consisted of a few very large enterprises. Ultimately these national companies were, in their turn, taken over by multi-national organisations, which, because of their size and reach, were able to do business globally.

We can see this process playing out in the ownership of the Wells site as it moved from Scophony to Scophony Baird, EMI Engineering, Thorn, Racal, Thomson-CSF, and finally Thales. However, these changes of ownership, and continual restructuring within each company, were not directly related to any failure in the performance of the Wells site. Indeed the unique team of scientists, engineers and skilled craftsmen that had grown up at Penleigh was recognised by all of its many owners as a valuable asset.

Although changing the name on the door must have kept the local sign-writers in business, the team that worked at Penleigh, and the projects with which they were involved, were remarkably consistent throughout its life. The balance between R&D and production work may have changed but that was all.

Its various owners saw the relatively small Penleigh site, not as some anonymous factory producing whatever it was told, but rather as a valuable, independent unit – a coherent and consistently successful team that functioned smoothly across its various disciplines. And it remained just such a team until the curtain finally came down in November 2011.

But life at the site did not exist in isolation.

In major industrial centres people seldom see their fellow workers outside of work, but in a city of 10,000 people, an enterprise with so many employees could not help but weave itself into the fabric of the city. Wells came to rely on the Penleigh site, and in many ways the site was equally dependent on the city.

Workers from senior management to machine-shop apprentices were part of the same community, together enjoying Field Days, Open Days, and the many delights of the EMI Social Club. In many ways the unique situation at Wells could not help but make the company more of a family firmly embedded in its community, than its counterparts in Birmingham, Manchester or London.

Now the Penleigh site is empty and what will replace Thales is unclear.

Rather than mourn the passing of such a remarkable group of people, and their unusual workplace, we should acknowledge and celebrate its many achievements – achievements that were to play an important role in the defence of our country, and our armed forces' success when forced to go to war.

That a temporary development, adapted from an equally temporary prisoner-of -war camp, should have remained successful for so many years is not due to the buildings at Penleigh, but to the remarkable group of people who generation after generation designed and produced so much of the technology that we as civilians, and our armed forces' have come to rely on.

The story of the Penleigh site and its workforce, is one that the people of Wells and the Somerset Levels have every reason to be proud of.

And finally ...

Farewell from us!

Photo by David Titchener

A special thank you to the following for their research and assistance.

Alan Cook
Alan Roper
Arnold Arnold
Bernard Franklin
Bernie Mundy
Betty Clements
Brian Jackson
Brian Prewer
C.H.E. Clements (Clem)
Colin Radford
Dave Morgan
David Grover
Denis Hurd
Don Franklin
Ernie Cashen
Gordon Newbery
Gordon Selby
Grace Bamford
Harry Smith
Jane Linthorne
Jim Tomlinson
John Entwistle
John Prout
Jon Hutton
Malcolm Plaster
Mary Harrington
Mike Coniford
Mike Penery
Peter Farrent
Phyllis Spacey
Ray Spacey
Richard Moon
Rose Townsend
Steve Cousins
Terry Delaney
Terry Ellaway
Tim Haskins
Tim Wallis
Tony D'ovidio